Methuen's Monographs on Physical Subjects
General Editor : B. L. WORSNOP, B.Sc., Ph.D.

WAVE MECHANICS

WAVE MECHANICS

BY

H. T. FLINT
Ph.D., D.Sc.

PROFESSOR OF PHYSICS IN THE UNIVERSITY OF LONDON,
BEDFORD COLLEGE

WITH 20 DIAGRAMS

LONDON: METHUEN & CO. LTD.
NEW YORK: JOHN WILEY & SONS, INC.

First published January 31st 1929
Second edition, revised April 1931
Reprinted 1938, 1944, 1946, 1950, 1951
Eighth edition, revised 1953

8.1

CATALOGUE NO. 4035/U [METHUEN]

PRINTED IN GREAT BRITAIN

PREFACE

THIS little book is written in the hope that it will be of assistance to those who are interested in the most recent development of physics ; the new method of approach to atomic problems.

The aim has been to present to the reader in a reasonably simple manner an account of the theory, with its relation to existing physical theory, as developed by de Broglie and Schrödinger. This theory is properly called Wave Mechanics, and it is based on conceptions of continuity. It is in fact a classical theory, for the methods adopted are those which were familiar to physicists before the beginning of this century. The mathematical analysis required has been extensively developed by earlier generations of physicists and may be regarded as part of a familiar equipment. For this reason the theory is approached by ways that the physicist of to-day may not have explored before, but which are well mapped out and amply provided with sign-posts.

No attempt has been made to describe more than one of the two methods of studying these problems. The second has originated with Bohr, Dirac and Heisenberg and is fundamentally different in character, for it is based on a conception of discontinuity and is called The New Quantum Mechanics. The mathematical analysis in this case is less familiar to physicists, is less developed and some of it new.

We do not wish to appear to regard one view as more important or more powerful in dealing with these problems than the other. It is too early in the history of the new developments to take sides and to some extent preference for the one or the other view is a matter of taste. It is remarkable that two views so widely different should lead to the same results, and though the reason for this may be easily explained by a comparison of the notations employed, we must not lose sight of the fundamental difference in physical character.

The list of references to original and other works printed at the end of the book is given in the hope that it will be of help to those who wish to consult original papers, and also as an acknowledgment of the sources which have been drawn upon in writing the book. In addition we must acknowledge also two lectures by Prof. E. T. Whittaker given in the course of the last year.

H. T. F.

WHEATSTONE LABORATORY
   KING'S COLLEGE
      LONDON
December, 1928

PREFACE TO THE SECOND EDITION

SINCE the first edition of this book was written there have been great advances both in theory and practice in the branch of physics with which it deals.

It has been necessary to make alterations in this edition, to omit certain parts and to add others.

The chapter on the experimental work has been re-written in order to include some of the newer work and to omit some of the older which was unsatisfactory.

In the theoretical work the principal addition is that of the equations of the first order.

In the past two years a number of important books on this subject have appeared, and there is now a considerable literature at hand for those interested in it.

In a book of this size it is possible to select only a few parts of the subject and to try by means of them to show the character of the new methods applied to the study of fundamental phenomena.

The purpose has been to offer to those who have not yet found time to study the subject in detail, and to those who are beginning it, a short account of the main features, and an introduction to original papers and larger works.

H. T. F.

WHEATSTONE LABORATORY
   KING'S COLLEGE
      LONDON
March, 1931

PREFACE TO THE EIGHTH EDITION

IN this edition the monograph has been largely re-written but the original purpose of presenting the principles, on which the subject of Wave Mechanics is founded, has been preserved.

The chapter on the experimental verification of the theory is almost in its original form. The decision not to alter this part of the work appreciably has been made because the early experiments are simple, direct and conclusive. They are also of historical interest.

Modern accounts of work in the experimental field of this branch of physics are the subject of other publications in this series of monographs.

A new feature of this edition is the presentation of the ideas which led to Dirac's suggestion that an equation of the first order should form the basis of wave mechanical theory. This introduction is in keeping with the purpose of the book and it replaces the inelegant presentation which was at first proposed in order to avoid the use of the calculus of matrices. It has turned out, however, that this earlier treatment of the wave equation is not only inelegant but also incorrect, for it rests on an analogy between the equation of the quantum theory of the electron and those of the electromagnetic field. It has been evident for a long time that this analogy does not exist and any such presentation must be removed.

The introduction of the first order equation has required some account of the calculus of matrices but the account has been kept close to the immediate requirements. It is hoped that this brief account of the necessary operations will enable the reader to appreciate the nature and the important consequences of Dirac's work.

H. T. F.

BEDFORD COLLEGE
UNIVERSITY OF LONDON
November, 1951

CONTENTS

INTRODUCTION

UNTIL the beginning of the present century the development of theoretical physics had progressed so far and so successfully that the principles underlying natural phenomena seemed to be understood, and it was expected that the same principles would hold in any new domain of knowledge which might be discovered. Nowadays after half a century of further research we are familiar with the inadequacy of the wonderful structure which previous generations have built up and which we know as the classical theory. It will be worth while to consider briefly the development of this theory, and to glance at its far-reaching successes before pointing out where it proved inadequate.

It is well known that Newton was the first to work out the laws of dynamics, and this branch of knowledge became a self-contained domain as the result of his work and that of his successors. His law of gravitation immediately opened up a new field for the newly-established science in which it reaped, and still reaps, success after success. In the eighteenth and nineteenth centuries in the hands of mathematicians, astronomers and physicists, mechanics attained such a degree of elegance that the whole science could be founded upon a single principle known as the principle of least action, which was first developed by Maupertuis and later in a quite different way by Hamilton.

The principles of mechanics came to be applied extensively in hydrodynamics, in the theory of sound and in optics, and in each case with success. Later on the development of statistical mechanics by Maxwell, Boltzmann and Gibbs offered an explanation of the second law of thermodynamics which at first appeared to stand aside from the mechanical theory.

The mechanical theory of optics lost ground and was finally defeated altogether by the wave theory, the reaction occurring about the beginning of the nineteenth century.

Later in this century came the electromagnetic theory in which Maxwell combined the results of his predecessors into an exact theory and showed that optics was a branch of the theory of electromagnetism.

The century was distinguished also by the experimental work of Sir J. J. Thomson on the discontinuity of electricity, and by the introduction of the hypothesis of discontinuity into the Maxwellian theory by H. A. Lorentz.

The discovery of positive and negative charges and of their universal occurrence led one school of thought to the electrical theory of matter. If matter is ultimately electricity then the phenomena of Nature may be expected to be ultimately electromagnetic, and the forces experienced are electromagnetic in origin. One might anticipate that mechanics itself would turn out to be a branch of electromagnetism. The introduction of Lorentz's formula for the force on a moving charge to complete Maxwell's equations was a step towards joining up the mechanical and electromagnetic domain.

The state of affairs at the beginning of this century certainly justified the hope that there would be an early blending of these apparently separate domains into a unified physical territory.

The opening years of the century, however, brought to light a very serious difficulty. It proved to be one of many which the classical theory had to encounter. The interest in the union of existing theories was lost in the attempt to account by known principles for the experimental result now clamouring for explanation.

There were originally two clouds darkening the classical sky, with one of which we are not now concerned. This was the difficulty associated with the Michelson-Morley experiment which has been removed by the principle of relativity. This principle does not actually depart from the methods of classical physics, it embodies the same spirit and though it has brought an attitude to physical phenomena which is very far removed from that of our classical predecessors, it reveals the older theory as a close approximation to the new. No matter how differently one may regard the law of gravitation in the light of the general principle of relativity we can still describe Newton's law of gravitation as a first approximation and in fact a very close approximation. Nevertheless, it was natural to hope that the modification of Newtonian mechanics which came with the new theory would help to smooth away the difficulties.

The second difficulty indicated a breakdown in statistical mechanics. One of the consequences of this theory is the principle of equipartition of energy. This principle may be understood by considering the case of a molecule which moves without rotation in a collection of similar and similarly moving molecules. The kinetic energy corresponding to the x-co-ordinate of the particle is $\frac{1}{2}m\dot{x}^2$ where $\dot{x}$ denotes the velocity and m the mass of the particle. The principle of equipartition of energy states that the average value of $\frac{1}{2}m\dot{x}^2$ is the same as the average value of $\frac{1}{2}m\dot{y}^2$ and of $\frac{1}{2}m\dot{z}^2$ where y and z denote the other two co-ordinates. This value is in fact $\frac{1}{2}kT$, where k is Boltzmann's constant and T the absolute temperature.

In this case we have three co-ordinates which fix the position of the particle ; in general there may be any number to fix each unit of which the assembly is composed. The principle of equipartition states that the kinetic energy corresponding to each component has on the average the same value $\frac{1}{2}kT$. This result, which is an unavoidable conclusion from the classical theory, when applied to the problem of determining how the energy in radiation is distributed with respect to the wave-lengths leads to a contradiction with experiment. Although it is in agreement with the experimental findings in the case of long waves it is inaccurate in the case of short waves and leads to the result that the total energy density of radiation is infinite. This can have no physical meaning.

It was in attempting to explain on theoretical grounds this question concerning black body radiation that Planck introduced his quantum hypothesis which formed the starting-point of the old quantum theory. Another difficulty arose in that the classical theory of specific heats ed to the law of Dulong and Petit that the atomic heats of the elements were constant. There were important deviations from this theory which only received an explanation by the use of quantum principles which were additions to the classical theory and which could in no way be deduced from it.

The study of photo-electric phenomena brought to light the difficulty that electrons emitted from metals by radiation incident upon them came away with an energy dependent on the frequency and not upon the intensity of the incident rays. This received a theoretical explanation by Einstein by a principle again foreign to the classical theory.

In this way a theory grew up whose content appeared at variance with accepted views but which was applied to particular problems simultaneously with the classical theory and was therefore looked upon as an additional limitation to that theory.

The state of physics appeared to many who wrote on this subject about that time to be threatened with chaos, since one set of laws appeared to work well in one domain and another quite different set in another domain. H. Poincaré shortly before his death and after the Solvay Congress of 1911 showed that it was necessary to introduce some quite new principle into theoretical physics, viz. Planck's hypothesis.

The success of this new theory, which we now call the old quantum theory, was not yet so widespread as to make it acceptable to physicists in general, but its most brilliant success awaited it.

In 1913 Bohr published his atomic theory, and so opened the most striking epoch in the history of spectra. The success of that theory, developed later by a generalisation of his principles by Sommerfeld and W. Wilson, is well known. The application of Bohr's principles has turned the theory of spectra from being a collection of heterogeneous data into a well-ordered branch of physics, and the success has been so extensive and at the same time so accurate in detail that the serious difficulties were often overlooked which have finally caused a revolt, in which Bohr himself has taken a leading part.

As a result of the old quantum theory a corpuscular character was again attributed to radiation, energy being supposed to be associated with it in the form of quanta of magnitude $h\nu$, where ν is the frequency of radiation and h is Planck's constant ($6\cdot62 \times 10^{-27}$ units). With these quanta we must associate a mass $\dfrac{h\nu}{c^2}$ according to the principle that energy has mass, which is a consequence of the theory of relativity.

One of the most striking applications of this is that of A. H. Compton, who considers the problem of the scattering of radiation by electrons as if it were a problem of impact of quanta and electrons. His results are in agreement with experiment. On the other hand, in the phenomena of interference we are compelled to hold to the wave theory of light, and this is true even in the case of Röntgen rays as the crystal phenomena studied by Laue and by Sir William and W. L. Bragg amply show.

These different phenomena show that radiation has apparently both a corpuscular and an extended character, and the time has come to try to unite these apparently opposing aspects.

Two different lines of attack have been made upon these and other difficulties. One of them initiated by Heisenberg sought to describe the phenomena without considering any hypothetical details in the system considered. In observing the behaviour of electrons, protons and atoms we may say that what is observed consists of spectral frequencies, intensities and states of polarisation. We do not observe positions, velocities or frequencies in electronic orbits, and it is in our equations connecting these unobserved quantities that difficulties arise. Heisenberg proposed to omit these details from his equations and to develop a system of calculation in which only observed quantities occur. This method calls to mind the principle of relativity in which there is no mention of the aether. The aether is a medium whose properties escape observation, and in describing phenomena by the principle of relativity any mention of the aether is avoided.

In classical physics we have an example of a similar method of procedure in thermodynamics, and it is clear from experience that such methods are very powerful, outlasting the detailed methods in which a model is assumed.

Heisenberg's method led to the application of the matrix analysis to these problems, and at the same time, guided by the same principles, Dirac applied his notation.

The purpose in this book is, in the first place, to turn our attention to the work of de Broglie and Schrödinger. This consists in the association of a wave-like character with what have hitherto been regarded merely as corpuscles. In the old quantum theory of radiation a corpuscular character has been associated with radiation. We have become familiar with this double aspect in the case of radiation. De Broglie's work is an extension of this idea, and as a result of it we have come to associate particles and waves throughout the domain of physics, in mechanics as well as in radiation. Inspired by the work of de Broglie, Schrödinger has established an elegant theory from the principles of dynamics. His methods represent a return to classical methods, as we shall see in the following pages.

Finally a chapter is devoted to Dirac's theory which has introduced new methods and new views into this domain of physics. It has revealed Schrödinger's work as a classical approximation to a wider relativistic theory.

CHAPTER I

THE VARIATION PRINCIPLES OF DYNAMICS AND OPTICS

It is the purpose of this chapter to show that dynamics presents a close analogy to geometrical optics and that it can be extended in the same way that physical optics is extended from geometrical optics. This new branch of dynamics has come to be known by the name " wave mechanics."

The Principle of Least Action.—A particle with velocity v has a mass m given by

$$m = \frac{m_0}{\left(1 - \dfrac{v^2}{c^2}\right)^{\frac{1}{2}}},$$

m_0 denoting the rest mass of the particle and, if it is acted upon by a force, the equations of motion are

$$\frac{d}{dt}(mv_x) = X = -\frac{\partial V}{\partial x},$$

and two similar equations in y and z.

v_x denotes the x-component of velocity and X the x-component of the force. It is assumed that the force can be derived from a potential V. The components of momentum mv_x, mv_y and mv_z will be denoted by p_x, p_y and p_z and the variation of the integral

$$\int_{A_1}^{A_2} (p_x \, dx + p_y \, dy + p_z \, dz)$$

will be considered.

In the first place, let the meaning of the integral itself be considered.

For this purpose it is sufficient to consider the case of a single variable x and momentum p_x. Suppose that p_x and x are plotted as ordinate and abscissa for a single particle in motion. Any point on the line joining A_1A_2 in Fig. 1

can be considered to represent the mechanical state of the particle in that it records a sequence of values of position and momentum.

Any number of paths joining A_1 and A_2 may be drawn, one of them will represent the relation between the position and momentum for the case when the particle is in motion under the force X. The above equation of motion applies to this particular path, which is described as the mechanical path.

The same extension of this idea to the case of three dimensions can be imagined. It is necessary to imagine points labelled with the three components of momentum

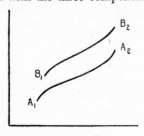

FIG. 1

and the three co-ordinates. This would require six independent axes so that it is easier to think of the analogy than to try to represent it diagrammatically.

Secondly, let the meaning of the variation of the integral be considered.

Suppose that the value of the integral for the path A_1A_2 has been found. Let B_1B_2 be a path infinitesimally close to A_1A_2. The difference between the integral for the path B_1B_2 and that for A_1A_2 is the variation of the integral for A_1A_2.

This variation is denoted by

$$\delta \int_{A_1}^{A_2} (p_x\, dx + p_y\, dy + p_z\, dz).$$

The quantities occurring in this expression are functions of the time t, and in order to see how the variation is carried out, suppose that ξ is a function of t, $\xi = f(t)$.

In fig. 2 let C_1C_2 represent the graph of ξ plotted against t and let D_1D_2 represent the function

$$\xi = f(t) + g(t),$$

where $g(t)$ is an infinitesimally small function of t, $g(t)$ is the variation of ξ from the former value on the curve $\xi = f(t)$. Thus $\delta\xi = g(t)$ and in determining $\delta\xi$ as a variation from the original path t is kept the same on the original and varied curves. Thus, referring to the figure,

$$\delta\xi = g(t) = PQ.$$

Although fig. 1 represents the values of p_x and x only, it

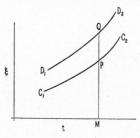

Fig. 2

will be supposed that the case considered is one of three dimensions, the co-ordinates of A_1 and A_2 being (x_1, y_1, z_1) and (x_2, y_2, z_2) respectively.

Let the co-ordinates of B_1 be $x_1 + \delta x_1$, etc., and of B_2 $x_2 + \delta x_2$, etc.

Consider the first term $\delta \displaystyle\int_{A_1}^{A_2} p_x \, dx$ of the variation. This is equivalent to $\displaystyle\int_{A_1}^{A_2} \delta(p_x \, dx)$ which can be written in the form

$$\int_{A_1}^{A_2} (\delta p_x \, dx + p_x \, \delta \, dx).$$

It must be remembered that in the change from one path to another dx like any other function undergoes a change δdx.

When a function ξ is changed to $\xi + \delta\xi$, $d\xi$ becomes $d\xi + d\delta\xi$, but by definition the change in $d\xi$ is $\delta d\xi$, so that $d\delta\xi = \delta d\xi$. This applies to x and dx so that $\delta dx = d\delta x$. Thus the second term in this integral can be written in the form $\int_{A_1}^{A_2} p_x \, d\,(\delta x)$ and on integrating by parts this becomes

$$\left[p_x \, \delta x \right]_{A_1}^{A_2} - \int_{A_1}^{A_2} dp_x \, \delta x.$$

The integrated portion is $(p_x \, \delta x)_{A_2} - (p_x \, \delta x)_{A_1}$ and since the displacements at A_1 and A_2 are δx_1 and δx_2 respectively, the value is

$$(p_{x_2} \, \delta x_2 - p_{x_1} \, \delta x_1)$$

It will be assumed in this discussion that there is no displacement at the beginning and end of the path, B_1 and B_2 being coincident with A_1 and A_2 respectively, but the path between A_1 and A_2 is displaced. In this case δx_2 and δx_1 are both zero and the variation takes the form

$$\int_{A_1}^{A_2} (\delta p_x \, dx - dp_x \, \delta x).$$

It will now be assumed that the original path is the dynamical path and consequently that the co-ordinates and momentum satisfy the equations of motion. In this case $\dfrac{dx}{dt}$ is the velocity of the particle v_x and $\dfrac{dp_x}{dt} = X = -\dfrac{\partial V}{\partial x}$.

Now $\delta p_x = \delta(mv_x) = v_x \, \delta m + m \, \delta v_x$, and

$$\delta m = \frac{m_0}{\left(1 - \dfrac{v^2}{c^2} \right)^{3/2}} \left(\frac{v_x \, \delta v_x + v_y \, \delta v_y + v_z \, \delta v_z}{c^2} \right).$$

$$= \frac{m_0}{\left(1 - \dfrac{v^2}{c^2} \right)^{3/2}} \frac{\Sigma v_x \, \delta v_x}{c^2}$$

$$\delta p_x \, dx = \delta p_x \frac{dx}{dt} \, dt = \delta p_x \, v_x \, dt = (v_x{}^2 \, \delta m + m \, v_x \, \delta v_x) \, dt.$$

Summing for the x, y and z terms and making the appropriate substitutions $\Sigma\, \delta p_x\, dx = c^2\, \delta m\, dt$.

The second term of the integrand

$$dp_x\, \delta x = \frac{dp_x}{dt}\, dt\, \delta x = -\frac{\partial V}{\partial x}\, \delta x\, dt$$

and summing for the three terms

$$\Sigma\, dp_x\, \delta x = -\Sigma \frac{\partial V}{\partial x}\, \delta x\, dt = -\delta V\, dt.$$

Thus $\displaystyle \delta \int_{A_1}^{A_2} (p_x\, dx + p_y\, dy + p_z\, dz) = \int_{A_1}^{A_2} \delta(mc^2 + V)\, dt.$

The expression $(mc^2 + V)$ represents the energy according to relativistic mechanics. The Newtonian expression for the kinetic and potential energy is $(\tfrac{1}{2}mv^2 + V)$ which is an approximation to $(m - m_0)c^2 + V$. This will be denoted by E so that

$$W = E + m_0 c^2 \qquad \qquad (1.1)$$

Thus writing $\delta W = \delta(mc^2 + V)$

$$\delta \int_{A_1}^{A_2} (p_x\, dx + p_y\, dy + p_z\, dz) = \int_{A_1}^{A_2} \delta W\, dt \qquad (1.2)$$

This is the relation which holds for the variation from the dynamical path to one slightly displaced from it. The variation vanishes if the same energy is associated with the two paths, for then $\delta W = 0$. Thus with this limitation together with the assumption that the initial and displaced paths have the same terminal points

$$\delta \int_{A_1}^{A_2} (p_x\, dx + p_y\, dy + p_z\, dz) = 0,$$

in other words the integral $\displaystyle \int_{A_1}^{A_2} \Sigma\, p_x\, dx$ has a stationary value. In the case of Newtonian mechanics, the mass being constant, $p_x\, dx = mv_x^2\, dt$, and, if T denote the kinetic energy, the variation becomes

$$\delta \int_{A_1}^{A_2} 2T\, dt = 0 \qquad \qquad (1.3)$$

$\int_{A_1}^{A_2} T\, dt$ is described as the action and the principle expressed by (1.2) is known as the principle of least action. The derivation given here shows that the action integral has a stationary value, not necessarily a minimum.

The principle of stationary action was stated by Moreau de Maupertuis in a memoir read in Paris in 1744. His statement of the principle was in the form: *When any change occurs in Nature, the quantity of action, necessary for this change, is the smallest possible.*

At the end of the same year Euler showed that in trajectories described under central forces the action was a minimum.

Hamilton's Principle. Since x is a function of the time t, it is possible to write

$$p_x\, dx = p_x \frac{dx}{dt}\, dt = p_x v_x\, dt.$$

Thus the variation of the integral $\int_{A_1}^{A_2} \Sigma\, p_x\, dx$ can be written in the form

$$\delta \int_{t_1}^{t_2} \Sigma\, p_x v_x\, dt = \Sigma\, (p_{x_2}\, \delta x_2 - p_{x_1}\, \delta x_1) + \int_{t_1}^{t_2} \delta W\, dt \qquad (1.4)$$

In this expression the variations at the ends of the path have been restored to include the general case when the two paths have different initial and final points and t_1 and t_2 denote the times corresponding to the points A_1 and A_2 respectively. The times for B_1 and B_2 are $(t_1 + \delta t_1)$ and $(t_2 + \delta t_2)$ respectively.

Consider the variation $\delta \int_{t_1}^{t_2} W dt$. This expression means the difference between the value of $\int_{t_1}^{t_2} W dt$ along $A_1 A_2$ and $B_1 B_2$, the value of W along $A_1 A_2$ being denoted by W and along $B_1 B_2$ by $W + \delta W$. Thus

$$\delta \int_{t_1}^{t_2} W\, \delta t = \int_{t_1 + \delta t_1}^{t_2 + \delta t_2} (W + \delta W) dt - \int_{t_1}^{t_2} W\, dt \qquad . \quad (1.5)$$

Remembering that δt_1, δt and δW are very small so that products of the form $\delta W \, \delta t$ can be neglected it follows that

$$\delta \int_{t_1}^{t_2} W \, \delta t = W_2 \, \delta t_2 - W_1 \, \delta t_1 + \int_{t_1}^{t_2} \delta W \, dt,$$

where W_1 and W_2 denote the values of W at A_1 and A_2 respectively. It will be supposed that the energy along the dynamical path is conserved so that W is constant and $W_1 = W_2 = W$. From (1.4) and (1.5) it can be deduced that

$$\delta \int_{t_1}^{t_2} L \, dt = \Sigma(p_{x_2} \, \delta x_2 - p_{x_1} \, \delta x_1) - W(\delta t_2 - \delta t_1), \quad (1.6)$$

where $L = \Sigma p_x v_x - W$.

The function L is described as the Lagrangian function.

If the initial and final points are the same for the dynamical and the displaced paths and if the times for these paths are the same, so that $\delta x_1 = \delta x_2 = 0$ and $\delta t_2 = \delta t_1$, the variation vanishes:

$$\delta \int_{t_1}^{t} L \, dt = 0. \qquad . \qquad . \qquad (1.7)$$

Thus a second principle is deduced expressed by the fact that the integral $\int_{t_1}^{t_2} L \, dt$ has a stationary value. This is known as Hamilton's principle and, like that of Maupertuis, it is subject to restricting conditions. It applies to the variation from a dynamical path to a neighbouring one with the same end points, the time intervals for the paths being the same.

In relativistic mechanics $L = mv^2 - W$, writing $p_x = mv_x$, etc., and, since $W = mc^2 + V$, it follows that

$$L = - m_0 c^2 (1 - v^2/c^2)^{\frac{1}{2}} - V \quad . \qquad (1.8)$$

In the case of Newtonian mechanics, it is convenient to introduce the energy E which denotes the sum of the kinetic and potential energies and thus to express L in the form:

$$L = mv^2 - E - m_0 c^2.$$

In the variation of the integral the term $m_0 c^2$, being constant, makes no contribution, so that L may be identified with $(mv^2 - E) = (T - V)$, since $mv^2 = 2T$ and $E = T + V$. In the Newtonian case the Lagrange function is equal to the difference between the kinetic and potential energies.

Generalized Co-ordinates. In establishing these stationary principles the co-ordinates (x, y, z) have been used and the motion of a single particle has been considered.

The principles can be established for extended bodies by regarding them as collections of particles.

The use of Cartesian co-ordinates is, however, not always convenient and they are by no means the most simple.

Collections of particles and bodies such as rods, rotators, consisting of one particle rotating about another, and also still more complicated structures can be described with regard to their position and orientation by means of a certain number of independent variables.

The position of a single point is most simply described by the co-ordinates x, y, z. In this case three co-ordinates are necessary and sufficient. The point is said to have three degrees of freedom.

If the position and orientation of a thin rod, AB, is to be described, the centre of gravity can be located by three co-ordinates x, y, z. But to describe the position and orientation further data are necessary. Let a vertical line be drawn through the centre of gravity G and let the vertical line lie in a plane S which is parallel to some fixed plane. Let a perpendicular be drawn from one end, B, of the rod to the vertical line and let the foot of the perpendicular be C. If the angle, θ, between the rod and the vertical is known and the angle ϕ, made by the plane GBC with the plane S, the position and orientation of the rod are defined. In this case, where the rod is thin, the possibility of rotation about its long axis is neglected.

The five co-ordinates, x, y, z, θ, ϕ are called the generalized co-ordinates of the rod, which is said to have five degrees of freedom.

In general a system has n degrees of freedom and the co-ordinates are denoted by $q_1, q_2, \ldots q_n$.

In the case of a particle the position is given by a set of values (x, y, z) and in the case of a system by a set $(q_1, q_2, \ldots q_n)$, the former is represented by a point in 3 dimensions, the latter, by analogy, by a point in n dimensions. This hypothetical n dimensional space can be regarded as a geometrical convenience but it is not to be given physical significance ; the phenomenon is still one of 3 dimensions.

The kinetic energy of the system can be expressed in terms of the generalized velocities, of which $\dfrac{dq_r}{dt}$ or $\dot{q}_r$ is typical, and in the important cases the kinetic energy T is quadratic in the $\dot{q}_r$'s.

The generalized momentum corresponding to a co-ordinate q_r is defined to be

$$p_r = \frac{\partial T}{\partial \dot{q}_r}, \qquad . \qquad . \qquad (1.9)$$

the differentiation being made with respect to $\dot{q}_r$, the other $\dot{q}$'s being regarded as constant in the operation.

These relations for the p's provide equations by means of which the $\dot{q}$'s can be expressed in terms of the p's so that T can be expressed in terms of the generalized momenta (p_r) and the generalized co-ordinates (q_r). This may be illustrated by the case of a particle moving in a plane about the origin. The polar co-ordinates r and θ correspond to q_1 and q_2.

$$T = \tfrac{1}{2}m\dot{r}^2 + \tfrac{1}{2}mr^2\dot{\theta}^2.$$

This may be written in the form

$$T = \tfrac{1}{2}m\dot{q}_1{}^2 + \tfrac{1}{2}mq_1{}^2\,\dot{q}_2{}^2.$$

Thus $p_1 = \dfrac{\partial T}{\partial \dot{q}_1} = m\dot{q}_1,\ \ p_2 = \dfrac{\partial T}{\partial \dot{q}_2} = mq_1{}^2\,\dot{q}_2$, and it follows that

$$T = \frac{1}{2m}(p_1{}^2 + p_2{}^2/q_1{}^2).$$

In this case T is quadratic in p_1 and p_2 and depends upon the co-ordinate q_1 only, but in general T is a function of all the p's and q's. The theorems considered for 3 co-ordinates can be extended to the case of n co-ordinates. It is necessary to express the kinetic energy T in terms of the q's and $\dot{q}$'s.

The points on a curve representing the state of a system such as that for a point in fig. 1 represent the values of the generalized co-ordinates and momenta and the theorem of Maupertuis has the same form as in the simple case with the same restrictions as before, viz. :

$$\delta \int_{A_1}^{A_2} T dt = 0.$$

While that of Hamilton takes the form

$$\delta \int_{t_1}^{t_2} L dt = 0,$$

where $L = \Sigma p_r \dot{q}_r - W$.

The importance of the Lagrangian function in mechanics can be illustrated by considering the case of a particle in a field of force with potential V.

The equation of motion for the direction x is

$$\frac{dp_x}{dt} = -\frac{\partial V}{\partial x}. \quad . \quad . \quad . \quad (1.10)$$

The function L in this case is

$$L = T - V = \tfrac{1}{2}m(\dot{x}^2 + \dot{y}^2 + \dot{z}^2) - V$$

$$\frac{\partial L}{\partial \dot{x}} = m\dot{x} = p_x, \quad \frac{\partial L}{\partial x} = -\frac{\partial V}{\partial x} \quad . \quad (1.11)$$

thus $\dfrac{d}{dt}\dfrac{\partial L}{\partial \dot{x}} - \dfrac{\partial L}{\partial x} = 0$, is identical with equation (1.10).

This is one of the Lagrangian equations of motion which apply also in the case of generalized co-ordinates. Generally $\dfrac{\partial L}{\partial \dot{q}_r} = p_r$, p_r and q_r being the conjugated momentum and co-ordinate.

In the case of the particle in the field with potential V the momentum $m\dot{x}$ is conjugate to the co-ordinate x. The case is somewhat different when the field of force differs from this as in the case of an electric charge, e, in motion in an electromagnetic field. In order to preserve the form (1.11) for the equation of motion in this case it is necessary to take as the value of L,

$$L = T - V + \frac{e}{c}(A_x \dot{x} + A_y \dot{y} + A_z \dot{z}), \quad (1.12)$$

where (A_x, A_y, A_z) are the components of the vector potential and V is the electrostatic potential multiplied by the charge ($V = e\phi$).

The field components of magnetic and electric intensity are given by

$$H = \text{curl } A, \quad E = -\text{grad } \phi - \frac{1}{c}\frac{\partial A}{\partial t}. \quad (1.13)$$

If the expression (1.12) is substituted in equation (1.11) the result is the equation of motion of the particle under the Lorentz force acting upon the charge e in an electromagnetic field.

The important point is that the momentum $m\dot{x}$ is no longer the conjugate of the co-ordinate x for the conjugates are $\dfrac{\partial L}{\partial \dot{x}}$ and x and evidently

$$\frac{\partial L}{\partial \dot{x}} = m\dot{x} + \frac{e}{c} A_x.$$

Thus writing

$$p_x = \frac{\partial L}{\partial \dot{x}} = m\dot{x} + \frac{e}{c} A_x \quad . \quad (1.14)$$

it is clear that the conjugate p_x is not equal to the momentum $m\dot{x}$ unless there is no electromagnetic field. It will be seen that this is of importance in the derivation of the fundamental equation of wave mechanics for an electric charge in an electromagnetic field.

General Equation of Mechanics.—Let the extreme value of the integral $\displaystyle\int_{A_1}^{A_2} \Sigma p_x \, dx$, taken along the mechanical path, be denoted by S.

2

According to equation (1.4)

$$\delta S = \Sigma(p_{x_2}\delta x_2 - p_{x_1}\delta x_1) + \int_{t_1}^{t_2} \delta W\, dt.$$

It is assumed that the energy W along the dynamical path is constant and also that the energy $W + \delta W$ along the neighbouring path is constant. Thus δW is constant and

$$\delta S = \Sigma(p_{x_2}\delta x_2 - p_{x_1}\delta x_1) + \delta W(t_2 - t_1). \quad (1.15)$$

Let it be supposed that x_1 and t_1 are fixed initial values and that x_2 and t_2 are replaced by x and t to denote any values appropriate to points on the path.

Thus

$$\frac{\partial S}{\partial x} = p_x, \quad \frac{\partial S}{\partial W} = t \quad . \quad . \quad (1.16)$$

and there are similar relations for y and z.

Similarly let

$$S' = \int_{t_1}^{t_2} L\, dt$$

on the mechanical path.

From equation (1.6)

$$\delta S' = \Sigma(p_{x_2}\delta x_2 - p_{x_1}\delta x_1) - W(\delta t_2 - \delta t_1),$$

and again taking x_2 and t_2 as any values for the path, it follows that

$$\frac{\partial S'}{\partial x} = p_x, \quad \frac{\partial S'}{\partial t} = -W \quad . \quad . \quad (1.17)$$

with similar relations for y and z.

The definitions of S and S' show that

$$S' = S - Wt. \quad . \quad . \quad (1.18)$$

It will be remembered that the integral which S denotes is taken between limits (x_1, y_1, z_1) and (x_2, y_2, z_2) along a path for which the energy is W.

Thus taking the first point as fixed and the second as variable, S is a function of x, y, z and W, and in the same way S' is a function of x, y, z and t. Suppose that the tracks of the particle considered are drawn for short intervals of time. Let the time for A_1A_2 be τ and for B_1B_2 $\tau + \delta\tau$ (fig. 1).

With the same notation as was used before, it is possible in this case to write

$$x_2 = x_1 + v_x \tau$$

v_x denoting the x-component of velocity, which remains appreciably constant over the small interval τ. For the displaced track $B_1 B_2$

$$x_2 + \delta x_2 = x_1 + v_x \tau + \delta x_1 + \delta(v_x \tau).$$

Thus $\delta x_2 = \delta x_1 + v_x \delta \tau + \tau \delta v$.

In general $S = \int_{t_1}^{t_2} \Sigma p_x v_x \, dt$ so that when applied to the short path

$$S = \Sigma p_x v_x \tau$$

and $$\delta S = \Sigma p_x v_x \delta \tau + \Sigma(p_x \delta v_x + v_x \delta p_x)\tau. \qquad (1.19)$$

But from equation (1.15)

$$\delta S = \Sigma(p_{x_2} \delta x_2 - p_{x_1} \delta x_1) + \delta W \tau.$$

and substituting $p_{x_2} = p_{x_1} + \dot{p}_{x_1} \tau$ together with the expression for δx_2.

$$\delta S = \Sigma(\dot{p}_x \delta x + p_x \delta v_x + \delta W)\tau + \Sigma p_x v_x \delta \tau \qquad (1.20)$$

where τ^2 and $\tau \delta \tau$ are regarded as negligibly small and x_2 is replaced by x as the current co-ordinate.

From equations (1.19) and (1.20)

$$\delta W = \Sigma(v_x \delta p_x - \dot{p}_x \delta x).$$

Thus

$$\frac{\partial W}{\partial p_x} = v_x, \quad \frac{\partial W}{\partial x} = -\dot{p}_x \qquad . \qquad . \qquad (1.21)$$

with similar relations in y and z.

These six equations are known as the canonical equations. The same form for the canonical equations is preserved in the case of generalized co-ordinates. W is expressed in terms of the co-ordinates and momenta and if, as will be supposed, it does not depend upon the time explicitly, this dependence is expressed by writing

$$H(q_1, p) = W,$$

where q and p represent all the co-ordinates $q_1, q_2, \ldots q_n$ and all the momenta $p_1, p_2, \ldots p_n$.

The canonical equations for each q and p are

$$\frac{\partial H}{\partial p} = \dot{q}, \quad \frac{\partial H}{\partial q} = -\dot{p} \qquad . \qquad (1.22)$$

From equations (1.17) in their generalized form

$$\frac{\partial S'}{\partial t} + H(q, p) = 0$$

and $p = \dfrac{\partial S'}{\partial q}$.

Thus S' satisfies the equation

$$\frac{\partial S'}{\partial t} + H\left(q, \frac{\partial S'}{\partial q}\right) = 0 \qquad . \qquad (1.23)$$

This is known as the Hamilton-Jacobi equation and the solution of the mechanical problem is reduced to the solution of this equation.

The importance of these general considerations in the development of the quantum theory is that the form of the equations has served as a guide in setting up a theory of quantum mechanics.

The Variation Principle of Optics.—The optical principle corresponding to the mechanical principles just considered is older than these and is known as Fermat's principle. This states that a ray of light in passing from a point A_1 to a point A_2 describes a path for which the time of transit has a stationary value. If the phase velocity of light is denoted by U and an element of the path by ds the principle is expressed by

$$\delta \int_{A_1}^{A_2} \frac{ds}{U} = 0 \qquad . \qquad (1.24)$$

The relation holds for a variation from the optically possible path to a neighbouring one with the same initial and final points.

It is possible to derive the laws of reflection and refraction from this principle so that it can be recognized as a fundamental principle of geometrical optics just as the mechanical principles are fundamental in dynamics.

CHAPTER II

THE ANALOGY BETWEEN THE MECHANICAL AND OPTICAL PRINCIPLES

THE stationary theorems of mechanics and optics suggest that a similar formal mathematical treatment may apply to both these branches of physics.

The analogy had not passed unnoticed by earlier mathematicians and physicists. Maupertuis, who was familiar with Fermat's principle, sought to overcome some difficulties which occupied men of his day on the subject of the velocity of light in media denser than air by applying his theorem to rays of light.

In 1744 he wrote a memoir on *The Harmony of different Laws of Nature which have hitherto appeared incompatible*, in which he tried to replace Fermat's principle by the statement : *The path which light takes is that along which the quantity of action is least.*

It is more generally known that Hamilton laid stress upon this analogy.

But until about 1925 optics had advanced in a direction which appeared to have no counterpart in mechanics.

In optics the geometrical theory was known to fail in cases where the wave-length of light was of the same order of magnitude as the dimension of the objects upon which it fell. The subject of physical optics, which includes the phenomena of interference and diffraction, had been developed by the wave theory of light and its relation to the phenomena of geometrical optics was understood. A theory of optics existed which included both geometrical and physical optics.

In mechanics, however, although it was known from the work of Bohr, Einstein and Planck that the laws of mechanics on a small scale differed from those on a large scale, the treatment at first consisted in accepting, in general, the known laws of classical mechanics and supplementing them by additional rules or laws which appeared as limitations to the general theory.

It was not until 1924 that the significance of the analogy began to be understood. At this time L. de Broglie put forward the idea that a wave-length was to be associated with a particle. He was convinced that it was necessary to create a new mechanics closely connected with the theory of waves and in 1926 Schrödinger, in a paper entitled: *Quantization as a Problem of Proper Values*, put into expression the analogy which was considered in the first chapter. The principle on which he worked was that just as geometrical optics requires extension if the field of physical optics is to be considered, so classical mechanics must be extended if quantum phenomena are to be described. The basis of physical optics is the wave equation so that the problem is to discover the wave equation in quantum mechanics. In electromagnetism, optics, sound and in other branches of physics propagation by waves is a familiar feature. The phenomenon under consideration is represented by a wave function F which satisfies the wave equation

$$\nabla^2 F - \frac{1}{u^2} \frac{\partial^2 F}{\partial t^2} = 0 \qquad . \qquad . \quad (2.1)$$

F may denote a component of the intensity of the electromagnetic field, a particle displacement or some other appropriate quantity. The symbol u is a quantity with the dimensions of velocity and may be complex.

The solutions of the wave equation which are of importance in physics are of the form

$$F = A \cos 2\pi(\theta - vt), \qquad . \qquad . \quad (2.2)$$

Where the amplitude A and the quantity θ depend on the space co-ordinates only.

It is convenient in some cases to regard more complicated forms of F as made up of a Fourier summation of such sinusoidal terms, each of which satisfies the wave equation, and this is an important feature of all wave theories, including wave mechanics.

A simple form of θ is one in which it is linear in the co-ordinates. It is usually written in the form

$$\theta = \frac{lx + my + nz}{\lambda}.$$

The wave is then said to be a plane wave and λ is the wave length.

The argument of the cosine term, $2\pi(\theta - vt)$, is described as the phase of the wave.

Suppose that at a certain time the phase has a certain value, it is then constant over the surface,

$$\theta = \text{constant},$$

known as the wave front, the constant having an appropriate value according to the time considered.

Let (x, y, z) denote a point on this surface. At a slightly different time $(t + dt)$ the phase will have the same value as at time t at a point $(x + dx, y + dy, z + dz)$ provided that

$$\Sigma \frac{\partial \theta}{\partial x} dx - v \, dt = 0.$$

This may be written in the form $\dfrac{\partial \theta}{\partial n} dn - v \, dt = 0$, where dn denotes an element of the normal to the wave front at the point considered. Thus to keep up with a surface of constant phase it is necessary to travel along the normal to the family of surfaces, $\theta = \text{constant}$, with the velocity

$$U = v \left/ \frac{\partial \theta}{\partial n} \right. \qquad . \qquad . \qquad (2.3)$$

The curves normal to these surfaces are described as rays. In order to determine the relation between this velocity, described as the phase velocity and the quantity u of the wave equation, it is convenient to consider the complex quantity

$$F' = Be^{2\pi i(\phi - vt)}$$

where B is a constant and ϕ is the complex quantity $(\theta + i\chi)$. The solution (2.2) is the real part of F' provided that $A = Be^{-2\pi\chi}$. F' is a solution of the wave equation if

$$2\pi i \nabla^2\phi - 4\pi^2 \sum \left(\frac{\partial\phi}{\partial x}\right)^2 + 4\pi^2\frac{\nu^2}{u^2} = 0 \qquad (2.4)$$

If the sum of the second differential coefficients of ϕ is small in comparison with the sum of the squares of the first differential coefficients,

$$\sum \left(\frac{\partial\phi}{\partial x}\right)^2 = \frac{\nu^2}{u^2} \quad . \quad . \quad . \quad (2.5)$$

If ϕ is real and thus equal to θ, A is constant and equal to B and by equation (2.5) u is real.

In this case $\sum\left(\dfrac{\partial\phi}{\partial x}\right)^2 = \sum\left(\dfrac{\partial\theta}{\partial x}\right)^2 = \left(\dfrac{\partial\theta}{\partial n}\right)^2$ and from (2.3) and (2.5) $u = U$.

From equation (2.3) $\theta = \displaystyle\int \frac{\nu}{U}\,dn$ and the approximate solution of the wave equation is

$$F = B\cos 2\pi\nu\left(\int\frac{dn}{U} - t\right) = B\cos 2\pi\left(\int\frac{dn}{\lambda} - \nu t\right), \quad (2.6)$$

where $\lambda = U/\nu$ is the wave length.[1]

The condition of equation (2.5) now becomes

$$\frac{\partial\theta}{\partial n} = \frac{\nu}{U} \quad . \quad . \quad . \quad (2.7)$$

and the neglect of the second differential coefficients in comparison with the sum of the squares of the first in equation (2.4) means that the ratio

$$\left| \frac{\partial^2\theta}{\partial n^2} \middle/ \left(\frac{\partial\theta}{\partial n}\right)^2 \right| \ll 1$$

or assuming that the frequency remains constant

$$\left| \frac{\lambda}{U}\frac{\partial U}{\partial n} \right| \ll 1.$$

A simple physical interpretation of the relation is obtained by introducing the refractive index, μ, which is inversely

[1] L. de Broglie, *Journ. de Phys.*, 1926, **7**, 321.

proportional to the phase velocity U. The condition is thus

$$\left| \frac{\lambda}{\mu} \frac{\partial \mu}{\partial n} \right| \ll 1.$$

The element dn normal to a phase surface is an element of a ray which travels with varying phase velocity so that its path is that of a ray in a medium of varying refractive index. Over a surface through a point P let the index have the value μ and let the ray fall on the surface at an angle of incidence i. The law of refraction in the medium is

$$\mu \sin i = \text{constant}$$

or

$$\frac{d}{dn}(\mu \sin i) = 0,$$

μ being a function of the position along the ray.

Thus $\dfrac{1}{\mu} \dfrac{d\mu}{dn} = - \cot i \dfrac{di}{dn}$ and the condition now becomes

$$\left| \lambda \cot i \frac{di}{dn} \right| \ll 1.$$

$\dfrac{di}{dn}$ is the deviation of the ray per unit length and leaving aside the special cases when the ray is normal to the surface of constant refractive index ($i = 0$) and when it falls upon it at grazing incidence $\left(i = \dfrac{\pi}{2} \right)$, the relation means that the deviation must be small in the distance of a wave length. Since the deviation of the ray per unit length is the reciprocal of its radius of curvature this is only another way of stating that the radius of curvature must be large in comparison with the wave length. It is under these circumstances that the principles of geometrical optics can be applied so that (2.7) is the condition of the validity of geometrical optics.

This discussion on the wave equation leads to certain important relations between mechanical and wave quantities by means of the analogy between mechanics and optics.

In equation (2.6) the expression $\int \dfrac{dn}{U}$ occurs as part of the phase. It is a function of the co-ordinates and is the expression which, in Fermat's theorem, has a stationary value, since dn denotes an element along the ray. The integrand may be written in the form $(l\,dx + m\,dy + n\,dz)/U$ where (l, m, n) are the direction cosines of the ray at the point (x, y, z), care being taken not to confuse the direction cosine n, with the element of the ray denoted by dn.

The quantity which corresponds to this expression in mechanics is the function $S = \int \Sigma p_x dx$, which also depends on the co-ordinates and does not contain the time explicitly. The expression $S' = S - Wt$ thus has the same form as the phase in the expression (2.6).

The fact that the relation $W = h\nu$ is fundamental in the quantum theory is also significant in making the comparison. It should be remembered that the phase is a quantity without dimensions while S' has the dimensions of the product of energy and time, that is to say of action. Thus before making use of S' as an argument in a sinusoidal function it must be divided by a quantity which has the dimensions of action. Comparison with expression (2.2), remembering the relation $W = h\nu$, suggests, the factor $2\pi/h$ as the first choice for this quantity. Thus the wave function of mechanics by this analogy is

$$F = B \cos \frac{2\pi S'}{h} = B \cos \frac{2\pi}{h}(S - Wt)$$

$$= B \cos \frac{2\pi}{h}\left(\int \Sigma p_x dx - Wt \right).$$

The phase $\dfrac{2\pi}{h}\left(\int \Sigma p_x dx - Wt \right)$ can be written in the optical form

$$2\pi\left(\int \frac{dn}{\lambda} - \nu t \right) = 2\pi\left(\int \frac{l\,dx + m\,dy + n\,dz}{\lambda} - \nu t \right)$$

by writing $W = h\nu$, $p_x = \dfrac{hl}{\lambda}$, $p_y = \dfrac{hm}{\lambda}$, $p_z = \dfrac{hn}{\lambda}$ (2.8) or, if p denote the total momentum,

$$p = \frac{h}{\lambda}. \qquad . \qquad . \qquad . \qquad (2.9)$$

This procedure thus introduces a frequency and a wave length into mechanics and the equations express relations between these quantities and mechanical quantities.

The relation between frequency and energy was introduced into the quantum theory by Planck at its beginning but that between wave length and momentum was suggested by de Broglie nearly a quarter of a century later. It is interesting to recall that the frequency relation was originally interpreted as the association of a particle like character with a wave. As de Broglie has said, it took much longer for physicists to associate a wave-like character with a particle.

The suggestion now is that a wave equation should be sought to correspond to that of optics which will form the basis of mechanics on the small scale.

The Wave Equation.—The surfaces of constant phase in the case of mechanics become surfaces over which the function S' has a constant value. The wave front is the surface $S = $ constant, corresponding to $\theta = $ constant in the case considered. Thus in order to keep up with the same phase it now becomes necessary to travel along the normal to the wave front, $S = $ constant, with the velocity

$$U = h\nu \Big/ \frac{\partial S}{\partial n} \qquad . \qquad . \qquad (2.10)$$

since S/h replaces θ in this case.

But from equations (1.16) it follows that $\dfrac{\partial S}{\partial n}$ is equal to the momentum p along the normal so that

$$U = W/p \qquad . \qquad . \qquad (2.11)$$

This result may be obtained by means of equations (2.8) and (2.9) from which

$$U = \nu\lambda = W/p.$$

The wave equation is thus

$$\nabla^2\psi = \frac{1}{U^2}\frac{\partial^2\psi}{\partial t^2}$$

and assuming that the wave function ψ contains t in the form $e^{-2\pi i\nu t}$ with $W = h\nu$, the equation becomes

$$\nabla^2\psi + \frac{4\pi^2}{h^2}p^2\psi = 0 \qquad . \qquad . \quad (2.12)$$

In classical mechanics $E = W - mc^2$ denotes the total energy and if V is the potential energy the appropriate approximate relation is

$$p^2/2m = E - V.$$

Thus the wave equation for this case is

$$\nabla^2\psi + \frac{8\pi^2 m}{h^2}(E - V)\psi = 0 \quad . \qquad . \quad (2.13)$$

This is Schrödinger's equation for the classical case.

In the mechanics of the special theory of relativity, in which $m = m_0/\sqrt{1 - v^2/c^2}$,

$$W = mc^2 + V$$

$$p^2 = m_0{}^2c^2\left\{\left(\frac{W - V}{m_0 c^2}\right)^2 - 1\right\} . \qquad . \quad (2.14)$$

and the wave equation takes the form

$$\nabla^2\psi + \frac{4\pi^2 m_0{}^2 c^2}{h^2}\left\{\left(\frac{W - V}{m_0 c^2}\right)^2 - 1\right\}\psi = 0 \quad (2.15)$$

The equation (2.13) may be derived from this as an approximation when the kinetic energy $(E - V)$ is small compared with the rest energy $m_0 c^2$. In this case $\left(\frac{E - V}{m_0 c^2}\right)^2$ can be neglected in comparison with the first power of this ratio.

Equation (2.12) can be examined in the same way as equation (2.1) in order to find the condition corresponding to that which must be satisfied when the methods of geometrical optics are applicable.

The phase being now $2\pi(S - Wt)/h$, the function ϕ in the condition (2.5) is replaced by S/h. Thus for the mechanical case

$$\sum \left(\frac{\partial S}{\partial x}\right)^2 = \frac{h^2\nu^2}{U^2} = p^2.$$

In the classical case this reduces to

$$\sum \left(\frac{\partial S}{\partial x}\right)^2 = 2m(E - V). \qquad . \qquad (2.16)$$

The equation of Hamilton and Jacobi (1.23) reduces to this relation when the energy is constant, for, expressed as a function of the co-ordinates and momenta,

$$H = \frac{1}{2m} \Sigma p_x^2 + V = E.$$

Thus

$$H\left(q, \frac{\partial S'}{\partial q}\right) = \frac{1}{2m} \sum \left(\frac{\partial S}{\partial x}\right)^2 + V$$

since

$$\frac{\partial S'}{\partial q} = \frac{\partial S'}{\partial x} = \frac{\partial S}{\partial x}.$$

Moreover $\dfrac{\partial S'}{\partial t} = W = E$ in the classical case so that (1.23) becomes

$$\frac{1}{2m} \sum \left(\frac{\partial S}{\partial x}\right)^2 = E - V. \qquad . \qquad (2.17)$$

The Hamilton-Jacobi equation is thus valid under the conditions when the methods of geometrical optics apply.

In deriving the relation (2.5) it was assumed that the second differential coefficients of ϕ were small in comparson with the square of the first. Since ϕ is replaced by S/h, the condition in the mechanical case is satisfied if h can be regarded as small.

Wave mechanics and ordinary mechanics thus coincide where it is possible to treat h as a vanishingly small quantity. This is impossible in the study of quantum phenomena so that here the two branches of mechanics are revealed as distinct.

It is interesting to compare the form of the wave equation (2.13) with that of equation (2.17). It appears that if the expression $\left(\dfrac{\partial S}{\partial x}\right)^2$ be replaced by $\left(\dfrac{h}{2\pi i}\dfrac{\partial}{\partial x}\right)^2\psi$ and $(E-V)$ by $(E-V)\psi$, the latter is transformed into the former. The momentum component p_x is replaced by $\dfrac{h}{2\pi i}\dfrac{\partial}{\partial x}$ and the expression $E = \dfrac{1}{2m}\Sigma p_x{}^2 + V$ becomes the operator

$$H = \frac{1}{2m}\sum\left(\frac{h}{2\pi i}\frac{\partial}{\partial x}\right)^2 + V.$$

The wave equation is then obtained by writing

$$H\psi = E\psi.$$

This is an example of the representation of physical quantities by operators which is an important feature of wave mechanics. It has led to an important change of view on the appropriate notation for the quantitative description of physical phenomena.

The Mechanical Wave Length and Atomic Dimensions.—In optics the geometrical methods fail when the objects lying in the path of rays of light have linear dimensions which are of the same order as the wave-length of the light. The analogy between mechanics and optics suggests that a similar breakdown will occur in problems where the dimensions become small.

It is in atomic phenomena that the need for a modification of mechanics has been suggested and it is in connection with atomic processes that the need for the quantum theory with the introduction of Planck's constant, has been necessary. The simplest case is that of the hydrogen atom where the orbital radius of the electron in the normal state is, by Bohr's theory, given by

$$a = h/2\pi p.$$

The wave length associated with the electron is $\lambda = h/p$ so that the radius is of the order of magnitude of the wave length.

Thus as physical optics comes to the aid of geometrical optics in phenomena such as those of diffraction, so it is to be expected that wave mechanics will be helpful in atomic mechanics.

The Elimination of the Energy Parameter from the Wave Equation.

In the derivation of the wave equation in mechanics it has been assumed that the time occurs in the factor $e^{-2\pi i \nu t}$. Thus the wave equation (2.13) is an equation for the part of ψ independent of the time, the wave function being obtained by multiplying the solution by this exponential factor. The equation may be described as the amplitude equation. It contains the parameter, E, which is constant for a particular value of ψ but differs for different ψ's. The function ψ is said to represent a particular state in which the energy is E.

It appears that equation (2.13) is a special case of a more general equation which it is desirable to discover.

In the case considered $\dfrac{\partial \psi}{\partial t} = -2\pi i \nu \psi$ and writing $V\psi = -\dfrac{h}{2\pi i}\dfrac{\partial \psi}{\partial t}$ or, in the classical case $E\psi = -\dfrac{h}{2\pi i}\dfrac{\partial \psi}{\partial t}$ since $W = h\nu$ or $E = h\nu$, the suggestion is that E be replaced by the operator $-\dfrac{h}{2\pi i}\dfrac{\partial}{\partial t}$. In the case of relativistic mechanics this operator will represent W. Thus the more general equation suggested is

$$\nabla^2 \psi + \frac{4\pi i m_0}{h}\frac{\partial \psi}{\partial t} - \frac{8\pi^2 m_0 V}{h^2}\psi = 0 \qquad . \quad (2.18)$$

is regarded as a function of the co-ordinates and time not necessarily limited to the particular form hitherto assumed. In this particular case it reduces to equation (2.13) but it is of wider application and is especially important in the theory of perturbations. ψ is in general a complex quantity and the equation in ψ^*, the complex conjugate of ψ is of equal importance with equation (2.18). This equation is :

$$\nabla^2\psi^* - \frac{4\pi i m_0}{h}\frac{\partial\psi^*}{\partial t} - \frac{8\pi^2 m_0 V}{h^2}\psi^* = 0 \qquad . \quad (2.19)$$

The discussion leading to equations (2.18) and (2.19) shows that it is of the same fundamental importance in wave mechanics as the wave equation in optics. It can also be regarded as the starting point in this branch of mechanics, just as Newton's laws or the principles of Maupertuis and Hamilton are the starting points of ordinary mechanics.

CHAPTER III

THE SIGNIFICANCE OF THE WAVE FUNCTION

In the familiar applications of the wave equation in physical problems the wave function, which has been denoted by F and by ψ in the previous chapter, can be related to some physical quantity. In the case of waves in air for example, the function represents the displacement of the air particles and in the case of light the function would formerly have been said to represent the displacement of particles of the aether. In the electromagnetic theory of light the wave function represents some quantity characteristic of the wave such as an electric or magnetic field intensity.

In the usual discussion of sound waves we describe the characteristics of the wave as being the pitch, quality and loudness or intensity, the last of these being proportional to the square of the amplitude. The question immediately rises as to the meaning of intensity in the case of the mechanical wave.

If intensity in this case has any significance it will naturally be measured by the square of the amplitude of the wave function. In the case in which the time occurs in the exponential form only, the intensity will be proportional to $|\psi|^2$ or $\psi\psi^*$ where ψ is a solution of equation (2.13). The difficulty is to associate the idea of intensity with the particle, or particles, described by the wave equation.

This particular difficulty is a fundamental one and it is only another form of the difficulty presented by the observation that electromagnetic waves present both a wave-like and a particle-like character. This dual nature is shown in the case of light and X-rays by the phenomena of interference and diffraction, on the one hand, and by the photo-electric and Compton effects on the other. In

3

this case it is the wave character which has made itself
the more obvious. In the case of particles the wave-like
character has not been very easily appreciated. But there
was finally evidence enough to show that there exists in
nature a duality expressed by the fact that a certain entity
may appear sometimes as a wave and sometimes as a
particle. In optics, for example, light may behave as if it
consisted of waves in one phenomenon and as if it consisted
of particles in another. Similarly, an electron may behave
in some cases as if it were a particle and in others as if it
were a wave.

In the early stages of this discovery the attempt to discover a union in this apparent duality proved very difficult,
although the relation between the particle characteristics of
energy and momentum could be related quantitatively with
the contrasting wave characteristics of frequency and wave
length by the relations of Einstein and de Broglie. An
interpretation of the wave function by Born has resolved
the difficulty.

Familiar examples of calculation of intensities occur in
optics in the study of interference patterns. Usually the
main interest lies in the location of the maxima and minima
in such distributions of intensity as occur in Newton's rings
or near the focus of a lens but sometimes a closer examination is necessary in order to determine how the intensity
falls off between maxima and minima as in questions of
the visibility of the patterns. If the light is considered as
a shower of photons the intensity in any region is proportional to the number of photons per unit area falling there.
This suggests that in the case of particles a similar interpretation might be given to $\psi\psi^*$. In the case of a shower
of particles, electrons for example, moving in a field of
force or being scattered by small objects, the number
falling in a particular place per unit area, or the intensity of
the pattern produced, is assumed to be proportional to the
square of the modulus of the wave function. The similarity of the wave equations applied in optics, including
X-rays, and mechanics accounts for the similarity of the
patterns observed. This interpretation is satisfactory in

the case of a large number of particles but appears difficult to apply to cases where the particles are few in number or even single. It might appear to suggest that an electron after being scattered by a small obstacle was to be found spread out over the whole pattern and this would not agree with observation.

This is the difficulty explained by Born's suggestion. According to this, it is impossible to say precisely where the single particle will fall after its encounter with the scattering object. The idea of the older theories that it is possible to treat the problem according to determinate methods must be regarded as inapplicable and at best an approximation. All that can be done is to deduce where the particle may fall and what chance it has of falling there. This chance, or probability, is measured by $\psi\psi^*$. In the case of many particles they will be found to be densest where $\psi\psi^*$ is greatest. They will be spread out so that they follow the variation of $\psi\psi^*$ and thus lie according to the intensity patterns of optics.

There was at first a considerable discussion on the question of the reality of mechanical waves but Born's suggestion puts the question aside. The wave-like character of particles is essentially due to the fact that the probability function ψ satisfies a wave equation. This is the explanation of the duality which at first was difficult to understand.

The probability of an event is usually expressed by a fraction so that it is natural to adjust the product $\psi\psi^*$ in accordance with this representation. Suppose that a particle moves in a region where the potential is V. The wave function then satisfies Schrödinger's equation (2.13). The probability of finding the particle in the element of volume $dx\,dy\,dz$ which contains the point (x, y, z) is defined as $\psi\psi^*\,dx\,dy\,dz$. Since the particle exists somewhere in the total volume under consideration it is convenient to apply some appropriate factor to ψ so that $\int \psi\psi^*\,dx\,dy\,dz$ is made equal to unity. This process is described as the normalization of the wave function.

A quantity, X, associated with the particle under conditions in which the wave function is ψ is said to have an average value of $\int \psi \psi^* X \, dx \, dy \, dz$.

The Uncertainty Relations.—In adopting a wave equation for the study of the behaviour of particles certain general results common to wave theories are taken over, which require an interpretation in the new field of their application.

In following up this idea Bohr and Heisenberg have revealed a very striking result. The ideas underlying this development are based upon Rayleigh's theory of optical instruments. This theory is familiar to students of physics in the form of some simple examples which will be used to illustrate the derivation of Bohr and Heisenberg's results.

A familiar example in the theory of sound leads to one of these results.

Suppose that two sources of sound emit notes of frequencies ν and $\nu + \delta\nu$ respectively, $\delta\nu$ being a small number compared with ν. Beats are heard of frequency $\delta\nu$. If the occurrence of beats is relied upon in order to appreciate the difference of frequency, at least one beat must be heard before it can be observed that the frequencies are different. Thus a certain time, δt, is taken up by the observation which is of the order of magnitude $1/\delta\nu$. This can be denoted by the relation

$$\delta t \, \delta\nu \sim 1. \qquad . \qquad . \qquad (3.1$$

A similar relation must hold in the case of any wave phenomenon provided the principle of superposition is accepted.

A similar condition is illustrated by means of the consideration of the expression for the resolving power of a grating. This is expressed by $\lambda/\delta\lambda$ and in the case of the grating

$$\frac{\lambda}{\delta\lambda} = Nn, \qquad . \qquad . \qquad (3.2$$

where N is the number of elements taking part in the diffraction and n is the order of the diffracted image.

Suppose that a parallel beam of rays falls normally on the grating and leaves it after transmission in the direction AC, the beam emerging from AB (fig. 3).

Since the diffracted beam is of the nth order, $AC = Nn\lambda$, λ being the wave length of the light.   Thus

$$\frac{\lambda^2}{\delta\lambda} = AC.$$

The meaning of the relation (3.2) is that no smaller difference of wave length can be observed in the order n

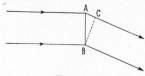

FIG. 3

with the grating.   It can be said that in order to resolve waves differing in wave length by $\delta\lambda$,

$$AC \sim \frac{\lambda^2}{\delta\lambda}.$$

Thus the wave train required in the resolution must be of length $\delta s = AC$, such that

$$\delta s \, \delta\left(\frac{1}{\lambda}\right) \sim 1. \qquad . \qquad . \qquad (3.3)$$

In a plane wave the phase is $2\pi\left(\dfrac{lx + my + nz - vt}{\lambda}\right)$ and thus $\dfrac{l}{\lambda}, \dfrac{m}{\lambda}, \dfrac{n}{\lambda}$ can be regarded as the components of a vector $\dfrac{1}{\lambda}$, known as the wave number.   In fact the components $\left(\dfrac{l}{\lambda}, \dfrac{m}{\lambda}, \dfrac{n}{\lambda}, \dfrac{v}{ic}\right)$ form a four-vector.   In terms of the co-ordinates and components of the vector wave number.

$$\delta\left(\frac{l}{\lambda}\right) \sim 1, \quad \delta y \, \delta\left(\frac{m}{\lambda}\right) \sim 1, \quad \delta z \, \delta\left(\frac{n}{\lambda}\right) \sim 1 . \qquad . \qquad (3.4)$$

and the fourth relation is $\delta x_4 \, \delta\left(\dfrac{\nu}{ic}\right) \sim 1$ which is identical with (3.1) since $x_4 = ict$.

Although these relations have been deduced by reference to particular examples, they are of general application and are of fundamental importance in wave theories.

The significance of the relation (3.3) is that, if a wave train of length δs is available, no variation in wave number can be determined less than $\delta\left(\dfrac{1}{\lambda}\right)$ where $\delta s \, \delta\left(\dfrac{1}{\lambda}\right) \sim 1$. In wave mechanics, by making use of the relations between energy and frequency and momentum and wave length, the relations become

$$\delta W \, \delta t \sim h \qquad . \qquad . \qquad . \qquad (3.5)$$

$$\delta p_x \delta x \sim h, \quad \delta p_y \delta y \sim h, \quad \delta p_z \delta z) \sim h. \qquad . \qquad (3.6)$$

The physical meaning of these relations is that if there is an uncertainty of magnitude δW in the amount of energy change in a particle there is also an uncertainty, δt, in the time at which this change takes place, δW and δt being related by (3.5).

Similarly if the location of the particle is made to an accuracy δx, δy and δz in the co-ordinates, there is an inaccuracy in the corresponding conjugate momenta given by (3.6).

These relations emphasize the contrast between the old mechanics and the new. It was formerly assumed that the co-ordinate x could be determined exactly, together with the momentum p_x.

The new point of view is that if a method of observation allows x to be determined within the limit of accuracy measured by δx, the momentum cannot be determined more accurately than δp_x in the formula (3.6).

This point has been illustrated by Heisenberg in an imaginary experiment designed to locate the position of an electron by means of gamma rays.

It is known that the error in determining the position of a particle in a microscope is of the order of the wave-length.

Two points cannot be resolved or recognized as distinct

by means of a lens if they are closer together than λ/A, where λ is the wave-length and A is the aperture or the angle subtended by the lens at either of the two points. The error in location is thus of order λ/A.

Let it be imagined that radiation is used to locate an electron in this way. The experiment and apparatus are, of course, purely imaginary, but the location of the electron may be said to be by means of gamma rays since gamma rays have very short wave-lengths.

The error δs in the determination of the position of the electron is of the order λ/A,

$$\delta s \sim \lambda/A.$$

The rays which fall upon the electron give it momentum, for the Compton effect occurs and a momentum $h\nu/c$ is

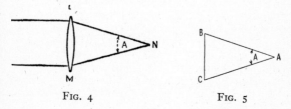

FIG. 4   FIG. 5

attributed to the radiation. Part of this momentum is taken up by the electron when the radiation falls upon it. The direction of the radiation lies within the angle A and the direction is not known more accurately than this. Thus the direction of the momentum of the photon lies between the direction of LN and MN. If the momentum corresponding to these directions is represented by AB and AC, the uncertainty in the momentum of the photon is of the order of magnitude of BC. In the interaction between the photon and electron, in which there is a transfer of momentum to the electron, there will be an uncertainty in the magnitude of the change in the momentum of the latter of this order of magnitude. Since

$$BC = AB \times \text{angle } A,$$

assuming A to be small and since $AB = h\nu/c$ the uncertainty δp in the momentum of the electron is

$$\delta p \sim h\nu A/c.$$

Thus $\delta p\, \delta s \sim h$, since $\nu\lambda = c$.

This uncertainty in the position and momentum of the electron, inherent in the process of their determination, illustrates the application of the relations (3.6) which apply to all particles. The example taken brings out the point that the uncertainty arises from the disturbance introduced in the process of measurement.

In observations of phenomena on a large scale the smallness of h makes it appear that both δp and δs can be measured to a degree of accuracy limited only by the sensitivity of the apparatus used and data are thus assumed to be available for carrying out calculations concerning the past and future behaviour of mechanical systems.

A fundamental change in principle is revealed by the discovery of the uncertainty relations (3.5) and (3.6) which show that it is impossible to determine exact values of both position and momentum. It is thus not possible to accept the principle of determinacy as it is implied in classical mechanics. The data for carrying out the classical scheme are not available.

It is perhaps natural to lay stress on the fact that the indeterminacy relations destroy the prophetic quality of classical physics but the essential feature is that the present cannot be completely known.

The idea of an inherent uncertainty at the basis of physical problems suggests the importance of taking a statistical view of them and the recognition of the wave function as a probability function is in harmony with the new point of view which the uncertainty relations have opened up.

Phase and Group Velocity.—It has been shown that the phase velocity associated with the wave function is given by

$$U = \frac{W}{p}.$$

In the case when there is no field of force and the particle has a mass m, the energy, W, according to the theory of relativity is mc^2. Thus

$$U = \frac{c^2}{v} \qquad . \qquad . \qquad . \qquad (3.7)$$

and since v, the velocity of the particle is less than c, the phase velocity is greater than the velocity of light. The fact that the phase velocity is of this magnitude is not in conflict with the fact that in the theory of relativity c is a limiting velocity. It is limiting in the sense that no material or energy can be transported at a greater velocity but no material is transported at the phase velocity.

The idea of a refractive index can be introduced in association with the wave function in the usual way, the index μ being defined in accordance with the relation

$$\mu = \frac{c}{U} = \frac{v}{c}.$$

Writing $\lambda_0 = \frac{h}{m_0 c}$ and $\lambda = \frac{h}{mv}$ it follows, since

$$m = m_0 \bigg/ \sqrt{1 - \frac{v^2}{c^2}}, \text{ that}$$

$$\mu^2 = \frac{\dfrac{\lambda_0{}^2}{\lambda^2}}{1 + \dfrac{\lambda_0{}^2}{\lambda^2}} \qquad . \qquad . \qquad . \qquad (3.8)$$

The refractive index is thus dependent upon the wavelength. The wave function thus behaves as in the case of waves in a dispersive medium.

A simple form of a wave function is

$$\psi = A e^{2\pi i (kx - vt)} \qquad . \qquad . \qquad . \qquad (3.9)$$

This is the complex form representing a monochromatic sinusoidal plane wave travelling in the direction of the axis of x, v is the frequency and k the wave number $\left(\dfrac{1}{\lambda}\right)$.

A group of waves consists of a superposition of such waves with frequencies continuously distributed over a small range on both sides of a frequency ν_0 and wave number $\frac{1}{\lambda_0}$.

The amplitude for each monochromatic wave will in general depend on the frequency and the wave function obtained by superposition of the members of the group is

$$F = \Sigma A_\nu e^{2\pi i(kx - \nu t)},$$

where A_ν is the amplitude for the wave of frequency ν. For the case of a continuous range of frequencies the amplitude for the range $d\nu$ is written in the form $A_\nu d\nu$ and the total wave function is

$$F = \int_{\nu_0 - e}^{\nu_0 + e} A_\nu e^{2\pi i(kx - \nu t)} \, d\nu, \qquad . \quad (3.10)$$

where the range of frequencies is from $(\nu_0 - \epsilon)$ to $(\nu_0 + \epsilon)$. The phase velocity is defined as the velocity with which it is necessary to travel in order to keep up with a constant phase. In the case of the wave of expression (3.9) this is ν/k The group velocity is defined as the velocity with which it is necessary to travel in order to keep up with a constant amplitude of the group.

If the small frequency range $(\nu - \nu_0)$ be denoted by $\Delta\nu$ and the small range of wave numbers $(k - k_0)$ by Δk, the expression (3.10) can be put in the form

$$F = e^{2\pi i(k_0 x - \nu_0 t)} \int_{\nu_0 - \varepsilon}^{\nu_0 + \varepsilon} A_\nu e^{2\pi i(\Delta kx - \Delta \nu t)} \, d\nu.$$

This is of the form

$$F = B e^{2\pi i(k_0 x - \nu_0 t)}$$

where the superposition of the wave group is represented as a simple wave of frequency ν_0 with an amplitude B.

If a point moves with the group so that its velocity is $w = \dfrac{\Delta\nu}{\Delta k} = \dfrac{d\nu}{dk}$ in the limit, it keeps up with the same total amplitude.

Thus the group velocity is

$$w = \frac{dv}{d\left(\frac{1}{\lambda}\right)} = -\lambda^2 \frac{dv}{d\lambda} = U - \frac{\lambda dU}{d\lambda} \quad . \quad (3.11)$$

making use of the expression $U = v\lambda$ for the phase velocity.

From (3.8) remembering that $U = \dfrac{c}{\mu}$, it then follows that

$$w = v. \quad . \quad . \quad (3.12)$$

The group velocity is thus equal to the velocity of the particle.

The suggestion arising from this is that the probability of presence of a particle is represented by a superposition of simple waves to form a group. If a particle is moving uniformly with a velocity v the probability of finding it at any place should be the same as that of finding it in the new place it has reached after travelling with this velocity. The group must keep up with the particle. The fact that a particle has of necessity a finite extent means that its probability of presence cannot be represented by a simple wave (3.9) which exists at all points and at all times. The wave function for a particle of finite extent must have a value in the region where the particle lies and must vanish rapidly at the edges of this region. The particle is represented by a probability packet.

The theory concerning the possibility of a superposition of waves so that the amplitude has a finite value within a region of space of dimensions δx, δy, δz shows that the following conditions must hold

$$\delta k_x \, \delta x \gg 1, \quad \delta k_y \, \delta y \gg 1, \quad \delta k_z \, \delta z \gg 1 \quad (3.13)$$

Further, if the duration of the group at a particular point is δt,

$$\delta v \, \delta t \gg 1. \quad . \quad . \quad (3.14)$$

If these relations be translated into the quantities appropriate to the mechanical waves they become

$$\delta p_x \, \delta x \gg h, \text{ etc.}$$
$$\delta W \, \delta t \gg h.$$

These are the uncertainty relations which occur here as the condition for the representation of the particle by means of a probability packet.

CHAPTER IV

THE NATURE OF THE PROBLEM AND THE SOLUTION OF SOME IMPORTANT EXAMPLES

THE problems which the adoption of a wave equation brings are not new to physics. The most attractive feature of the adoption of Schrödinger's equation for the solution of problems arising in the quantum theory was at first the return to classical methods. The title of Schrödinger's first paper, *Quantization as a Problem of Characteristic Values*, seemed hopeful to those who looked forward to the solution of the difficulties of the quantum theory in terms of classical ideas. Later developments have not led to the fulfilment of this hope.

The nature of the problem presented by the use of a wave equation can be appreciated by recalling a familiar example in the theory of sound. This is the example of a string fixed at its ends and under tension. It is required to find the displacement at a point at a distance, x, from one end at a time, t, after the string has been released from some originally known position.

If the displacement at this point at this time is y, the adoption of the wave equation which can be derived from the principles of mechanics, means that y satisfies the equation

$$\frac{\partial^2 y}{\partial t^2} = U^2 \frac{\partial^2 y}{\partial x^2} \qquad . \qquad . \qquad (4.1)$$

It is possible to find an infinite number of solutions to this equation, for it is clear that

$$y = A e^{ax + bt}$$

is a solution with no restriction upon A and only one relation between a and b, viz.: $b^2 = U^2 a^2$. Nevertheless, a unique solution to the problem can be found because of the boundary conditions attached to it.

Thus at all values of t the displacements and velocities at $x = 0$ and $x = l$ are zero, l denoting the length of the string. Moreover, the values of y and $\frac{dy}{dt}$ at all points of the string are initially given at $t = 0$, for the original form of the string is known.

So far in this account of wave mechanics a wave equation has been adopted but no boundary conditions have been stated. The boundary conditions imposed in this case are that the values of the wave function, ψ, must be everywhere finite, single valued and continuous and the function must approach the value zero at infinity. The functions, ψ, which satisfy these conditions are described as characteristic functions and it will be seen that each characteristic function is associated with a certain value of E (2.13). These values are described as characteristic values. Any particular problem consists in determining a value of ψ satisfying the conditions imposed.

The general method of approach to the solution of small scale problems before the introduction of quantum mechanics was by means of the assumption that the processes concerned followed courses like those which were observed on a large scale. It was assumed that the same mathematical processes could be applied in the quantitative description of the small and large scale phenomena. In the later stages of the period some modifications were introduced as in Bohr's theory applied to the atom. The small scale process was represented by a model. The best known of these was the Rutherford model and with the modifications of classical theories introduced into its quantitative description by Bohr there has been no more striking success of this method anywhere in physics. Indeed, for physicists at the time of greatest success, the model was thought to be identical with the atom. The essence of this process lay in the application of mechanics to the problems presented. Now that the belief in the existence of an atom possessing all the details of the model can no longer be held it becomes clear that the process was largely an appeal to the forms of mechanics to obtain equations accounting for observations in this branch of physics.

The point of view regarding the atom has changed. What remains of the model is a useful nomenclature. But the atomic electron can no longer be regarded merely as a point charge occupying a certain place in the atom. The electron is described by a function ψ and if some quantity concerning the electron is required, the appeal must be to ψ, just as at an earlier date the appeal would have been to the model. What is known about the electron is contained in the wave equation applicable to it. Later on it will appear that Schrödinger's equation (2.13) is to be replaced by another known as Dirac's equation, but the principle is the same.

These equations, and particularly Dirac's equation, represent the electron and can be described as the electron itself with as much right as the picture of a point charge.

One of the most important quantities in the study of the atom in the old quantum theory was the determination of the energy associated with a particular orbit or in another form the energy associated with a particular level.

From the new point of view this means the determination of the characteristic value, E_n, of the energy E associated with the appropriate characteristic function ψ_n.

There are certain features common to the solutions of the most important wave equations and these will be considered first before passing to the special cases.

The wave equation in these cases presents itself ultimately in the form

$$\frac{d^2y}{dx^2} + P\frac{dy}{dx} + Qy = 0, \qquad . \qquad . \quad (4.2)$$

where P and Q are functions of x.

This can be transformed into an equation which can be solved by means of a series. It will appear that the equation can be put into the form

$$(a_2x^{k+2} + b_2x^{l+2})\frac{d^2X}{dx^2} + (a_1x^{k+1} + b_1x^{l+1})\frac{dX}{dx}$$
$$+ (a_0x^k + b_0x^l)X = 0, \qquad . \qquad . \quad (4.3)$$

where k and l are whole numbers, a particular feature of the equation being that the difference between the powers of x is the same in each bracket.

It is convenient to write the equation in the form

$$x^k\left(a_2 x^2\frac{d^2X}{dx^2} + a_1 x\frac{dX}{dx} + a_0 X\right)$$
$$+ x^l\left(b_2 x^2\frac{d^2X}{dx^2} + b_1 x\frac{dX}{dx} + b_0 X\right) = 0 \quad . \quad (4.4)$$

By the introduction of the operator $x\dfrac{d}{dx}$, since

$$\left(x\frac{d}{dx}\right)^2 X = x^2\frac{d^2X}{dx^2} + x\frac{dX}{dx},$$

the first bracket of (4.4) may be written as

$$\left\{a_2\left(x\frac{d}{dx}\right)^2 + (a_1 - a_2)x\frac{d}{dx} + a_0\right\}X.$$

Thus with the notation

$$f(z) = a_2 z^2 + (a_1 - a_2)z + a_0$$

and
$$g(z) = b_2 z^2 + (b_1 - b_2)z + b_0$$

the equation (4.4) becomes

$$x^k f\left(x\frac{d}{dx}\right)X + x^l g\left(x\frac{d}{dx}\right)X = 0 \quad . \quad (4.5)$$

Assuming that $k > l$ and that $k - l = c$, a positive integer

$$x^c f\left(x\frac{d}{dx}\right)X + g\left(x\frac{d}{dx}\right)X = 0 \quad . \quad (4.6)$$

If $l > k$ an equation of a similar form results by dividing throughout by x^k.

The solution of equation (4.6) may be obtained by the method of integration by series (*Forsyth's Differential Equations*, Ch. V) and as much is reproduced here as is necessary for the present purpose, in order to deduce completely some of the most interesting results of the theory.

Let it be assumed that the function X can be expressed in the form of a series of powers of X.

$$X = A_1 x^{m_1} + A_2 x^{m_2} + \ldots,$$

where the m's are integral numbers arranged in ascending order and the A's are constants.

The method of solution consists in substituting the value of X in equation (4.6) and equating to zero the coefficients of the various powers of x. In this way the m's are determined and also the relations between the coefficients A. Finally, a solution is obtained containing the correct number of adjustable constants which in this case is two.

By referring to the forms of the functions f and g it appears that, on substituting for X, terms of the form $\left(x\dfrac{d}{dx}\right)^2 x^m$ and $\left(x\dfrac{d}{dx}\right) x^m$ will appear. These are respectively $m^2 x^m$ and $m x^m$, so that

$$f\left(x\frac{d}{dx}\right) x^m = f(m) x^m$$

and similarly for the function g.

Equation (4.6) thus gives

$$A_1 f(m_1) x^{m_1} + A_2 f(m_2) x^{m_2} + \ldots$$
$$+ A_1 g(m_1) x^{m_1-c} + A_2 g(m_2) x^{m_2-c} + \ldots = 0 \quad (4.7)$$

The lowest power of x in this equation is $(m_1 - c)$ and since the left-hand side must vanish identically the coefficient of x^{m_1-c} must vanish. Hence

$$g(m_1) = 0$$

for A_1 is not zero since it is assumed to be the coefficient of a term present in the series.

The roots of this equation give the values of m_1 with which the series begins and in the present case $g(m_1)$ is a quadratic so that the number is two.

On examining the other terms of the series it is found that a solution can be obtained in this way by equating the indices, thus :

$$m_1 = m_2 - c$$
$$m_2 = m_3 - c, \text{ etc.}$$

This is possible since the terms are arranged with indices in ascending order. The series therefore advances in powers of x differing by c.

Since the terms vanish identically, it follows that

$$A_1 f(m_1) + A_2 g(m_2) = 0$$
$$A_2 f(m_2) + A_3 g(m_3) = 0, \text{ etc.}$$

and from these equations all the coefficients may be obtained in terms of the first.

Let a be one of the values of m_1 with which the series begins, then

$$A_2 = -\frac{f(a)}{g(a+c)}A_1, \quad A_3 = \frac{f(a+c)f(a)}{g(a+2c)g(a+c)}A_1, \text{ etc.}$$

The solution is

$$X = A_1 x^a \left\{ 1 - \frac{f(a)}{g(a+c)}x^c + \frac{f(a+c)f(a)}{g(a+2c)g(a+c)}x^{2c} - \cdots \right\}$$

$$(4.8)$$

Since m_1 has two values, there is another solution of similar form multiplied by another constant.

The complete solution consists of the sum of these two. Certain complications may occur in the series, for a zero factor may occur in a factor of one of the coefficients. In some cases the series are infinite. It is not necessary to go into these cases in detail but there are two points to bear in mind. The first is that if one series terminates this corresponds to the occurrence of a line spectrum and the appropriate values of E are the corresponding energy levels.

If the series is infinite this corresponds to the existence of a continuous spectrum.

The condition that the series shall terminate is that $f(a)$, $f(a+c)$ or one of the functions occurring in numerators of the terms of the series (4.8) shall vanish.

A series $(U_1 + U_2 + U_3 + \ldots)$ is convergent provided that after some term in the series the ratio of one term to the next following is greater than unity, i.e. $\left| \dfrac{U_n}{U_{n+1}} \right| > 1$,

4

for values of n greater than some particular value. If this be applied to the series (4.8), the condition is

$$\left| \frac{g(a + \overline{n+1\,c})}{f(a + nc)} \cdot \frac{1}{x^c} \right| > 1.$$

Thus with the forms given above for the functions f and g this condition becomes

$$x^c < \left| \frac{b_2}{a_2} \right|$$

when n is large.

If the term in $a_2 x^{k+2}$ does not occur in the equation, the series is convergent for all finite values of x no matter how large.

In the cases to be considered $a_2 x^{k+2}$ does not occur in the differential equation, which can then be reduced to the form

$$\frac{d^2X}{dx^2} + \left(a_1 x^{s+1} + \frac{b_1}{x} \right) \frac{dX}{dx} + \left(a_0 x^s + \frac{b_0}{x^2} \right) X = 0, \quad (4.9)$$

where changes have been made in the meaning of the constants and $s = k - l - 2$.

To show that the wave equation in the form (4.2) can be reduced to the form of (4.9) write y in the form of the product FX.

On substituting $y = FX$ in equation (4.2) the equation becomes

$$\frac{d^2X}{dx^2} + \left(\frac{2}{F} \frac{dF}{dx} + P \right) \frac{dX}{dx} + \left(\frac{1}{F} \frac{d^2F}{dx^2} + \frac{P}{F} \frac{dF}{dx} + Q \right) X = 0$$

$$(4.10)$$

The boundary condition for the wave function will be satisfied if the function F approaches zero as x approaches zero with X a finite series.

In order that (4.10) should reduce to the form (4.9)

$$\frac{2}{F} \frac{dF}{dx} + P = a_1 x^{s+1} + \frac{b_1}{x}$$

$$\frac{F''}{F} + P\frac{F'}{F} + Q = a_0 x^s + \frac{b_0}{x^2},$$

writing F' and F'' for $\dfrac{dF}{dx}$ and $\dfrac{d^2F}{dx^2}$ respectively.

In the case when P and Q are polynomials $\frac{F'}{F}$ and $\frac{F''}{F}$ are also polynomials and consequently the differential coefficients must be divisible by F. Writing $F = e^{\phi}$ the function ϕ must satisfy

$$\left. \begin{array}{l} 2\phi' + P = a_1 x^{s+1} + \dfrac{b_1}{x} \\[2mm] \phi'' + \phi'^2 + P\phi' + Q = a_0 x^s + \dfrac{b_0}{x^2} \end{array} \right\} \quad (4.11)$$

ϕ' is thus a polynomial in x and if ϕ is a polynomial function in x with negative coefficients e^{ϕ} will approach zero as x approaches infinity and the boundary condition at infinity is satisfied.

It is not necessary to proceed to express F in terms of x in the general case, particular examples occur in the cases to be considered.

The Planck Oscillator.—The first example is one of historical interest because it is that to which Planck first applied his quantum postulate. In considering the problem of the interaction of radiation and matter he conceived the idea that certain simple harmonic oscillators formed the means by which energy in matter could be emitted as radiation and by which energy of radiation could be absorbed. The important feature of the process was that the energy of radiation was transmitted in certain amounts called quanta of magnitude $h\nu$, ν being the frequency of the radiation and also of the oscillators and h denoting Planck's constant.

The oscillator can be regarded as a particle of mass m vibrating along the axis of x under a restoring force proportional to the displacement, x, from the origin of co-ordinates.

The motion may be represented in classical mechanics by the equation

$$mx'' = -kx$$

and the solution is

$$x = A \sin(2\pi\nu t + \alpha), \quad . \quad . \quad (4.12)$$

where A and α are arbitrary constants and $4\pi^2\nu^2 = k/m$, ν denoting the frequency of the vibrations.

The potential energy is $\frac{1}{2}kx^2 = 2\pi^2\nu^2mx^2$.

Schrödinger's equation in this case is

$$\frac{d^2\psi}{dx^2} + \frac{8\pi^2m}{h^2}(E - 2\pi^2\nu^2mx^2)\psi = 0.$$

The energy equation of ordinary mechanics is

$$\frac{1}{2m}p^2 + 2m\pi^2\nu^2x^2 = E.$$

The wave equation results from replacing p by the operator $\frac{h}{2\pi i}.\frac{\partial}{\partial x}$ and then operating upon ψ in the following way :

$$\left\{\frac{1}{2m}\left(\frac{h}{2\pi i}.\frac{\partial}{dx}\right)^2 + 2m\pi^2\nu^2x^2\right\}\psi = E\psi.$$

On making the substitutions

$$a = \frac{8\pi^2mE}{h^2} \quad \text{and} \quad b = \frac{16\pi^4m^2\nu^2}{h^2},$$

the equation takes the simpler form :

$$\frac{d^2\psi}{dx^2} + (a - bx^2)\psi = 0 \qquad . \qquad (4.13)$$

This is of the type (4.2) and it can be converted to the form considered by means of the relations (4.11).

In the present case $P = 0$, $Q = a - bx^2$.

The object is to transform this equation so that the solution depends upon an equation of the form (4.3) or (4.9) which can be solved by series.

In accordance with the procedure described the function ψ is written in the form $e^\phi X$. On examining the conditions (4.11) in this case, bearing in mind that ϕ should take the form e^{-kx^n} with n positive, in order that this factor may approach zero as x approaches infinity, it is suggested that a satisfactory solution can be obtained by writing

$$s = 0, \quad b_0 = b_1 = 0.$$

The substitution of $\phi = \dfrac{a_1}{4} x^2$, derived from the first of the conditions (4.11), into the second, leads to

$$a_0 = a - b^{\frac{1}{2}}, \quad a_1 = - 2b^{\frac{1}{2}}.$$

It is necessary to choose the negative sign for a_1 in order to obtain a negative value for ϕ.

Thus $\psi = e^{-\frac{1}{2}b^{\frac{1}{2}}x^2}X$ and X is a solution of the equation

$$\frac{d^2X}{dx^2} - 2b^{\frac{1}{2}}x \frac{dX}{dx} + (a - b^{\frac{1}{2}})X = 0.$$

This is of the form (4.9) and can be solved by the substitution

$$X = \Sigma A_1 x^{m_1}$$

For convenience write $c = 2b^{\frac{1}{2}}$, $e = a - b^{\frac{1}{2}}$. It follows from the procedure for the solution by series that has been given that m_1 must take the values zero or unity and that in each case the series advances in powers increasing by 2. The coefficients are given in terms of the lowest by

$$A_2 = \frac{(cm_1 - e)}{(m_1 + 2)(m_1 + 1)} A_1,$$

$$A_3 = \frac{(c\overline{m_1 + 2} - e)(cm_1 - e)}{(m_1 + 4)(m_1 + 3)(m_1 + 2)(m_1 + 1)} A_1, \text{ etc.}$$

There is no difficulty when either the values 0 or 1 for m_1 are introduced for no term in the denominators vanishes.

It is now to be decided if the series terminate and this corresponds, as has been stated, to the occurrence of line spectra.

The series will terminate if one of the factors in the numerator vanishes, for if in advancing along the series any coefficient, A, vanishes, all succeeding coefficients vanish.

The factors in the numerator are of the form

$$c(m_1 + 2n) - e,$$

where n is a positive integer.

In the case $m_1 = 0$, this factor will vanish if

$$n = \frac{e}{2c}.$$

On inserting the values for e and c, it follows that the series will terminate if $E = (2n + \frac{1}{2})h\nu$. Again, considering the case in which $m_1 = 1$, it follows that the series will terminate if $E = (2n + 1 + \frac{1}{2})h\nu$. From these results the possible values of E are given by

$$E = (n + \frac{1}{2})h\nu,$$

where n is an integer, odd or even.

These values of the energy of the oscillator are interpreted as those which are physically possible.

The Rigid Rotator.—A case of importance in the theory of band spectra is that of the rigid rotator. This may be considered as two spheres with their centres joined by a rigid rod, the centre of one sphere being at a fixed point about which the system can rotate. If this point be taken as the origin of co-ordinates, the centre of the other sphere will move over a fixed spherical surface. The spheres may be regarded as masses, M, situated at their centres and no rotation about the line joining the centres is contemplated. There is no potential energy in this case and the wave equation is

$$\nabla^2\psi + \frac{8\pi^2 M E}{h^2}\psi = 0.$$

It is convenient to replace the co-ordinates (x, y, z) by polar co-ordinates (r, θ, ϕ) in this example.

The transformation of the Laplacian $\nabla^2\psi$ is readily made and the details will be found in mathematical text books. The transformed equation is

$$\frac{1}{r^2}\frac{\partial}{\partial r}\left(r^2\frac{\partial\psi}{\partial r}\right) + \frac{1}{r^2\sin\theta}\frac{\partial}{\partial\theta}\left(\sin\theta\,\frac{\partial\psi}{\partial\theta}\right) + \frac{1}{r^2\sin^2\theta}\frac{\partial^2\psi}{\partial\phi^2}$$
$$+ \frac{8\pi^2 m}{h^2}E\psi = 0 \quad (4.14)$$

In this case the mass M lies on a fixed sphere so that, writing $I = Mr^2$, the equation becomes

$$\frac{1}{\sin\theta}\frac{\partial}{\partial\theta}\left(\sin\theta\frac{\partial\psi}{\partial\theta}\right) + \frac{1}{\sin^2\theta}\frac{\partial^2\psi}{\partial\phi^2} + \frac{8\pi^2 IE}{h^2}\psi = 0 \quad (4.15)$$

A solution of this equation will be obtained in the form $\psi = \Theta\Phi$, where Θ depends upon θ only and Φ upon ϕ only.

On substituting for ψ, the equation can be put into the form:

$$\frac{1}{\Theta}\left\{\sin\theta\frac{\partial}{\partial\theta}\left(\sin\theta\frac{\partial\Theta}{\partial\theta}\right)\right\} + \frac{1}{\Phi}\frac{\partial^2\Phi}{\partial\phi^2} + \frac{8\pi^2 IE}{h^2}\sin^2\theta = 0.$$

The first and third terms are independent of ϕ so that the second term cannot depend upon it. Similarly the first and third terms together do not depend upon θ. The second term can thus be placed equal to a constant which will be denoted by $-m^2$. Φ is thus of the form

$$\Phi = A_m \sin m\phi + B_m \cos m\phi$$

and since Φ must be a single valued function, returning to the same value as ϕ increases by 2π, m must be an integer.

The equation is thus reduced to the form:

$$\frac{1}{\Theta\sin\theta}\frac{\partial}{\partial\theta}\left(\sin\theta\frac{\partial\Theta}{\partial\theta}\right) - \frac{m^2}{\sin^2\theta} = -\frac{8\pi^2 IE}{h^2} \quad (4.16)$$

There is a well-known solution of this equation when the right-hand side is in the form $-n(n+1)$, n integral. In the usual notation the solution is denoted by

$$\Theta = \sin^m\theta\, P_n{}^m(\cos\theta).$$

The function $P_n{}^m(\cos\theta)$ is the mth derivative with respect to $\cos\theta$ of the Legendre polynomial $P_n(\cos\theta)$.

There is thus a characteristic function $\Theta\Phi$ of the wave equation (4.15) with the characteristic value

$$\frac{8\pi^2 IE}{h^2} = n(n+1)$$

or

$$E = \frac{h^2}{8\pi^2 I}n(n+1). \qquad . \qquad . \quad (4.17)$$

The rigid rotator is a model which helps to picture the generation of the rotation spectra of molecules.

The energy state is labelled by the quantum number n and the emission is the result of transitions between certain energy states, the frequency of the radiation being calculated according to the quantum law—

$$E_n - E'_n = h\nu.$$

A selection rule applying to this transition must also be applied, which is $n \sim n' = 1$, but here only the determination of the energy value is under consideration.

The Line Spectrum of Hydrogen.—A problem of great importance is provided by the hydrogen atom and the energy values will be determined in this case.

The mechanical system in this case is imagined to consist of a central positive charge e which, in the present calculation, will be considered to be fixed, with an electron of charge e at a distance r from it. Since these charges are of opposite sign, the potential energy is $- e^2/r$ and the wave equation is

$$\nabla^2\psi + \frac{8\pi^2 m}{h^2}\left(E + \frac{e^2}{r}\right)\psi = 0, \qquad (4.18)$$

where m denotes the mass of the electron.

Expressing this equation in polar co-ordinates the following equation is obtained as in equation (4.14):

$$\frac{1}{r^2}\frac{\partial}{\partial r}\left(r^2\frac{\partial\psi}{\partial r}\right) + \frac{1}{r^2\sin\theta}\frac{\partial}{\partial\theta}\left(\sin\theta\,\frac{\partial\psi}{\partial\theta}\right) + \frac{1}{r^2\sin^2\theta}\frac{\partial^2\psi}{\partial\phi^2}$$
$$+ \frac{8\pi^2 m}{h^2}\left(E + \frac{e^2}{r}\right)\psi = 0 \quad (4.19)$$

A solution in the form

$$\psi = R\Theta\Phi$$

is sought in which R, Θ and Φ are functions of the single variables r, θ and ϕ respectively.

The equation can then be written in the form

$$\frac{1}{Rr^2}\frac{\partial}{\partial r}\left(r^2\frac{\partial R}{\partial r}\right) + \frac{1}{r^2}\left\{\frac{1}{\Theta\sin\theta}\frac{\partial}{\partial\theta}\left(\sin\theta\frac{\partial\Theta}{\partial\theta}\right) + \frac{1}{\Phi\sin^2\theta}\frac{\partial^2\Phi}{\partial\phi^2}\right\}$$
$$+ \frac{8\pi^2 m}{h^2}\left(E + \frac{e^2}{r}\right) = 0.$$

It follows, as in the case of the rigid rotator, that it is possible to place $\frac{1}{\Phi}\frac{\partial^2\Phi}{\partial\phi^2} = -m^2$ and to write

$$\frac{1}{\Theta}\sin\theta\frac{\partial}{\partial\theta}\left(\sin\theta\frac{\partial\Theta}{\partial\theta}\right) - \frac{m^2}{\sin^2\theta} = -l(l+1),$$

where m and l are integers.

Φ and Θ are thus well-known functions and a solution of the wave equation is

$$R\Phi\Theta = R(A_m\sin m\phi + B_m\cos m\phi)\sin^m\theta\,P_l^m(\cos\theta)$$
$$(4.20)$$

Thus R is a solution of the equation

$$\frac{d^2R}{dr^2} + \frac{2}{r}\frac{dR}{dr} + \left\{\frac{8\pi^2 mE}{h^2} + \frac{8\pi^2 me^2}{h^2 r} - \frac{l(l+1)}{r^2}\right\}R = 0$$
$$(4.21)$$

which is of the form (4.2).

In order to reduce this equation to the form (4.9) so that R may be obtained as a series the conditions (4.11) must be satisfied. It can be verified that this can be done by writing $s = -1$ and

$$\begin{aligned}\tfrac{1}{4}a_1^2 &= -\frac{8\pi^2 mE}{h^2}, & a_0 &= a_1 + \frac{8\pi^2 me^2}{h^2} \\ b_1 &= 2, & b_0 &= -l(l+1)\end{aligned}\Bigg\} \quad (4.22)$$

Thus R takes the form

$$R = e^{\frac{1}{2}a_1 r}X, \qquad . \qquad . \qquad . \quad (4.23)$$

where X is a solution of the equation

$$\frac{d^2X}{dr^2} + \left(a_1 + \frac{b_1}{r}\right)\frac{dX}{dr} + \left(\frac{a_0}{r} + \frac{b_0}{r^2}\right)X = 0 \quad (4.24)$$

In this case the functions f and g are respectively defined by

$$f(z) = a_1 z + a_0$$
$$g(z) = z^2 + z + b_0.$$

Thus the indices of r in the first terms of the two series are given by

$$m_1^2 + m_1 - l(l+1) = 0$$

or
$$m_1 = l \quad \text{or} \quad -(l+1)$$

and it appears that in this case $c = 1$.

The series beginning with $r^{-(l+1)}$ does not lead to a solution suitable to this particular case since the index of r is negative and $r^{-(l+1)}$ tends to infinity as r tends to zero. Thus considering the other series it is found to terminate if

$$f(a + pc) = 0 \quad \text{(p. 49),}$$

where p is an integer.

In the present case $a = l$ and the condition is

$$a_1(l + p) + a_0 = 0$$

or
$$p + l + 1 = 1 - \frac{a_0}{a_1}.$$

On substituting the values of a_0 and a_1 from the relations (4.22), this condition is seen to be

$$(p + l + 1)^2 = - \frac{2\pi^2 m e^4}{h^2 E}$$

and since p and l are integral this takes the form

$$E = - \frac{2\pi^2 m e^4}{h^2 n^2} \qquad . \qquad . \qquad (4.25)$$

where n is an integer.

These values of E for different values of n are identical with those of the theory of Bohr and Sommerfeld.

In Sommerfeld's theory the total quantum number n was made up of two numbers n' and k known as the radial and azimuthal quantum numbers which were related to the geometry of the orbit and which entered the theory through the quantum conditions of Sommerfeld and Wilson. I was later found to be more convenient to replace the azimuthal number k by $(l + 1)$, where l has the values o to $n + 1$). In the present theory l occurs naturally as an index of the Legendre function while n is a characteristic of the series denoted by R. The integer p introduced in the theory is the radial quantum number of the old quantum theory. This treatment of the problem gives no account of the fine structure of the lines of the spectrum and thus fails to account for those effects which the older theory attempted to explain by means of the principle of relativity and the assumption of the existence of electron spin.

The theory can therefore be described as the non-relativistic wave mechanical theory of the line spectrum of hydrogen. The negative value of E should be noted for this is a characteristic feature of the energy values in this case. It is required to give to the exponential factor in R of equation (4.23) the index which will cause this function to vanish at infinity ; a positive value of E would make a_1 imaginary. The values of E obtained in this way account for the Balmer series in the manner familiar in the old quantum theory.

The occurrence of quantum numbers in this problem and also in the case of the rigid rotator by a mathematical process without the use of special hypotheses such as mechanical limitations in a model is one of the attractive features of the wave mechanical approach to these problems.

The Theory of Alpha-Radioactivity.

—In the problems considered in this chapter no use of the wave function has been made. The solutions have been concerned with characteristic energy values. In the last example of this chapter a case is considered in which the wave function is required and its significance as a probability function will be illustrated.

This example is that of the passage of a charged particle through a potential energy barrier.

A problem of this kind is presented by the case of an alpha particle emitted from an atomic nucleus which is radioactive.

The field in the neighbourhood of an atomic nucleus is represented by the graph of the potential, V, at various distances, r, from the nucleus.

The general form of the potential is illustrated in fig. 6 showing that beyond a certain distance OA, the field falls off according to the inverse square law of Coulomb. From experiments on the scattering of α-particles in the case of heavy elements, it appears that this law holds to a distance of the order of 10^{-12} cm. from the nucleus. Within this distance of the nucleus the forces become attractive and the potential falls.

Suppose that the maximum potential, V_0, is reached at a distance OA from the nucleus. Any α-particle in the nucleus has to overcome this potential barrier if it is to escape from the nucleus. The usual dynamical theory teaches that unless the particle has at least the energy to overcome the potential V_0 it cannot get away.

In the case of uranium, α-particles are emitted with energies equal to their potential energy at a distance of $6\cdot3 \times 10^{-12}$ cm. from the nucleus, illustrated in the diagram by OB. Scattering experiments show that the inverse square law holds to within a distance of $3\cdot2 \times 10^{-12}$ cm. of the uranium nucleus where the potential is, of course, greater than that at $6\cdot3 \times 10^{-12}$ cm.

Thus since the α-particle was originally part of the nucleus it appears that it has escaped across a region where the potential energy is greater than its own energy. This is a serious difficulty for the usual theory of dynamics and it indicates that a new approach should be made to the problem.

According to wave mechanics, the problem is to find the probability that the particle will be found on the distant side of the potential barrier under the particular circumstances of the case.

The probability is obtained from the appropriate use of the wave equation.

In order to illustrate this problem a simpler distribution of potential than that which exists in the case of a nucleus will be considered.

The solution of the problem presented by radioactive processes is due to the work of Condon and Gurney and of Gamow.

Consider three regions, 1, 2, 3. In 1 and 3 the potential energy of the particle is taken to be zero and in 2 it is V_0.

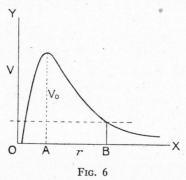

Fig. 6

A particle originally in region 1 is supposed to have energy $E < V_0$.

The problem is to discover the probability that a particle originally in region 1 will be found in region 3, the regions being separated by the barrier of region 2.

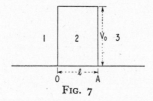

Fig. 7

The problem in this form is artificial but it is stated in this way because the principles of the calculation in the actual case can be illustrated by it and the solution is simple. Instead of the continuous rise and fall of the case of the atomic nucleus illustrated in fig. 6, there are discontinuous changes at O and A, fig. 7.

The point O will be taken as the origin of co-ordinates and A is at $x = l$.

The conditions are

$$V = 0 \text{ if } x < 0 \text{ or } > l,$$
$$V = V_0 \text{ if } 0 < x < l.$$

The wave equation for regions 1 and 3 is

$$\frac{d^2\psi_0}{dx^2} + \frac{8\pi^2 mE}{h^2}\psi_0 = 0 \qquad . \qquad . \quad (4.26)$$

This is the equation for the amplitude of the wave function ψ which contains the factor $e^{-2\pi i v t}$

$$\psi = \psi_0 e^{-2\pi i v t}$$

Writing $\alpha_1^2 = \dfrac{8\pi^2 mE}{h^2}$, the solution of equation (4.26) is

$$\psi_0 = A_1 e^{i\alpha_1 x} + B_1 e^{-i\alpha_1 x} \qquad . \qquad . \quad (4.27)$$

A similar equation with coefficients A_3 and B_3 applies to region 3.

In the central region the wave equation is

$$\frac{d^2\psi_0}{dx^2} + \frac{8\pi^2 m}{h^2}(E - V_0)\psi_0 = 0 \qquad . \quad (4.28)$$

In this case since $V_0 > E$ the substitution

$$\alpha_2^2 = 8\pi^2 m(V_0 - E)/h^2$$

will be made so that α_2 is a real number.

The solution in this case is

$$\psi_0 = A_2 e^{\alpha_2 x} + B_2 e^{-\alpha_2 x} \qquad . \quad (4.29)$$

In α-radioactivity it is observed that particles travel outward from the barrier in region 3 so that in the language of wave mechanics there is a certain probability that a particle travelling outward will be found in this region. The wave function expressing motion in this direction depends on the argument $2\pi(kx - vt)$, where v and k are the frequency and wave number $\left(k = \frac{1}{\lambda}\right)$.

Thus the problem is to find out whether a solution of the form $\psi_0 = A_3 e^{i\alpha_1 x}$ gives a definite amplitude A_3 from which the probability of occurrence $|A_3|^2$ can be obtained. In this region there is no reflection of particles by a barrier on the right of region 3, which is assumed to extend to infinity.

The particles in region 1 which fall on the potential barrier are partly reflected and partly transmitted. Thus in this region the particles are represented by the amplitude function (4.27), A_1 denoting the amplitude for particles travelling towards the potential barrier.

Thus the ratio $\dfrac{|A_3|^2}{|A_1|^2}$ is a measure of the probability that a particle will be transmitted across the barrier. In other words, it is the ratio of the number of particles crossing the barrier to those arriving at it.

Certain relations will be satisfied at the boundaries of these regions and, adopting those which are familiar in wave theories, they are :

$$\psi_{01} = \psi_{02}, \quad \frac{d\psi_{01}}{dx} = \frac{d\psi_{02}}{dx}, \text{ at } x = 0 \quad . \quad (4.30)$$

This means that ψ_0 in region 1 is equal to ψ_0 in region 2 at the boundary, that is to say, that the wave functions are continuous at the boundary, so also are the first differential coefficients.

Similarly,

$$\psi_{02} = \psi_{03}, \quad \frac{d\psi_{02}}{dx} = \frac{d\psi_{03}}{dx}, \text{ at } x = l. \quad . \quad (4.31)$$

The values of the amplitudes of the three wave functions are

$$\psi_{01} = A_1 e^{i\alpha_1 x} + B_1 e^{-i\alpha_1 x}$$
$$\psi_{02} = A_2 e^{\alpha_2 x} + B_2 e^{-\alpha_2 x}$$
$$\psi_{03} = A_3 e^{i\alpha_1 x}$$

and the boundary conditions (4.30) and (4.31) are

$$A_1 + B_1 = A_2 + B_2$$
$$i\alpha_1(A_1 - B_1) = \alpha_2(A_2 - B_2)$$
$$A_2 e^{\alpha_2 l} + B_2 e^{-\alpha_2 l} = A_3 e^{i\alpha_1 l}$$
$$\alpha_2(A_2 e^{\alpha_2 l} - B_2 e^{-\alpha_2 l}) = i\alpha_1 A_3 e^{i\alpha_1 l}$$

From these equations it can be deduced that

$$\frac{|A_1|^2}{|A_3|^2} = 1 + \frac{1}{4}\left(\frac{\alpha_2}{\alpha_1} + \frac{\alpha_1}{\alpha_2}\right)^2 \sinh^2 \alpha_2 l. \quad (4.32)$$

Suppose that $\alpha_2 l$ is large, then $\sinh^2 \alpha_2 l$ tends to the value $\frac{1}{4} e^{2\alpha_2 l}$ and on substituting for α_1 and α_2, retaining only the second term on the right-hand side, (4.32) reduces to the approximation

$$\frac{|A_3|^2}{|A_1|^2} = 16 \frac{E}{V_0}\left(1 - \frac{E}{V_0}\right) e^{-2\alpha_2 l} \quad . \quad (4.33)$$

Except when E/V_0 is zero or unity, the controlling factor in this expression is the exponential term.

In the simplified case considered α_2 is constant across the potential barrier but in the actual case, illustrated in fig. 6, this is not so. A more general argument shows that $2\alpha_2 l$ must be replaced by $J = \frac{4\pi}{h} \int \sqrt{2m(V_0 - E)} \, dx$.

In the case of an atomic nucleus the particles are originally in a region surrounded by a potential barrier illustrated by a surface generated by the rotation of the curve of figure 6 about the Y-axis. Suppose that a particle travels on the average over a distance d to and fro within the barrier. The frequency of its approach to the barrier is of the order of d/v, where v denotes its velocity. The probability of escape from the region is proportional to e^{-J}, so that the average time that elapses before escape is of the order $T = \frac{d}{v} e^J$. Within the barrier suppose that the potential energy is zero so that E is equal to the kinetic energy $\frac{1}{2}mv^2$ and $T = d\sqrt{\frac{m}{2E}} e^J$.

If the number of particles, N, is large the number escaping in time dt according to the law of radioactivity is

$$dN = - \lambda N \, dt.$$

This gives $N = N_0 e^{-\lambda t}$, and the average life of the substance is $\frac{1}{\lambda}$. The order of magnitude of $\frac{1}{\lambda}$ and T are the same and consequently $\lambda \sim e^{-J}$.

Radioactive elements show great differences in their rates of decay. Thus radium C' has an average life of a small fraction of a second, radium A of 4·4 minutes and uranium of 6000 million years.

Condon and Gurney have plotted curves for

$$\frac{4\pi}{h} \sqrt{2m(V_0 - E)}$$

against x, and have found values of J from areas under these curves on the graphs. Their results show that these great variations would be expected on the basis of this theory.

The empirical formula of Geiger and Nuttall relating the decay constant, λ, and the energy, E, of the α-particle emitted is

$$\log \lambda = a + bE,$$

where b is a constant for all the radioactive families and a is a constant peculiar to the family.

Gamow has shown that the wave mechanical treatment of α-radioactivity leads to this law.

5

CHAPTER V

EXPERIMENTAL EVIDENCE OF THE WAVE-LIKE CHARACTER OF MATTER

EXPERIMENT leaves no doubt about the existence of the corpuscular aspect of matter. The analogy between mechanical and optical theories called attention to the possible existence of a wave-like aspect.

The analogy suggests an experimental investigation which is to discover if particles show properties similar to those of photons.

According to de Broglie's formula experiments on particles should be undertaken to see if they behave as if they are associated with a wave-length

$$\lambda = \frac{h}{mv}, \qquad . \qquad . \qquad . \qquad (5.1$$

where mv is the momentum of the particle.

In experiments upon electrons this wave-length is of the same order as that of X-rays, and this suggests experiments on an electron beam similar to those that have been carried out on X-ray beams for the determination of X-ray wave lengths, e.g. diffraction by crystals and ruled gratings.

The earliest experiments of this kind which establish the wave-like character of electrons are those of Davisson and Germer.[1] Earlier work by Davisson and Kunsman carried out in 1923, suggests that there was already evidence for the wave nature of particles when the new theory appeared, but it is the opinion of Davisson that the results obtained at that time cannot be regarded as properly exhibiting the effect. The experiments of 1927 open

[1] *Nature*, 16th April, 1927 ; *Phys. Rev.*, 1927, **30**, 706.
[2] *Ibid.*, 1923, **22**, 1923.

new chapter in the history of experimental physics, and it is impossible to overstate their importance.

The electrons were emitted from a filament S, of heated tungsten ribbon, passed through slits to produce a narrow beam, and made to strike the target T normally. They were then collected in a receptacle C, which could move on an arc over such a range that beams could be received making angles between 20° and 90° with the incident beam. A sensitive galvanometer was connected to C and the deflections recorded were proportional to the number of electrons received. The potentials were arranged so that only those which had suffered a small loss of velocity at the target could enter the collector.

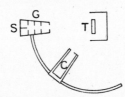

IG. 8.—Diagram illustrating Davisson and Germer's apparatus.

The bombarding current was of the order of a micro-ampere, and of this about 10^{-4} was diffracted to the collector. A sensitive galvanometer could readily detect a current of this magnitude. The bombarding potentials ranged from 15 to 350 volts.

The target could be rotated about an axis perpendicular to its surface so that various crystal planes could be made to pass through the collector. The three crystal planes concerned in the experiments were the (111), (110) and (100) planes (see Fig. 12). The collector was moved to various positions in these planes and the galvanometer current was plotted against the angle between the primary and diffracted beam (Fig. 8). This angle was described as the " colatitude ".

Fig. 9 shows the result obtained in the case of the (111) plane. As the voltages vary a peak appears at about 44 volts, and attains its greatest development at 54 volts in colatitude 50° (Fig. 9). If the voltages are increased the peak ultimately dies away, and there is hardly any trace of it at 68 volts.

If the crystal be rotated into the other two planes mentioned, small peaks are shown at 50° for 54 volts. These smaller maxima correspond to peaks, which reach their greatest development at other voltages and colatitudes.

Three different types of interference phenomena were detected : (a) scattering from a space lattice analogous to the X-ray phenomenon of Laue and Bragg ; (b) scattering from a "plane grating" arising from a single layer of atoms situated at the surface ; and (c) scattering from adsorbed

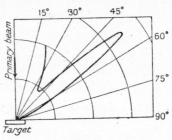

FIG. 9

gas on the surface of the crystal which was responsible for certain sets of observations. It was found possible to infer the structure of the gas film from them.

The type of interference under (b) is not observed in X-rays, and arises from the fact that electrons are much more readily absorbed than X-rays. They result from a preponderance of first layer scattering at angles near grazing emergence.

The results of the observations show that there is a correspondence with Laue-Bragg beams which would issue from the same crystal if the electrons were X-rays, and that there is an analogy with optically diffracted beams from plane gratings.

Thus we have striking qualitative evidence in favour of the wave-like character of electrons.

The radii to the curve measured from the target are proportional to the number of electrons collected in the corresponding directions.

The results turn out to be also in quantitative agreement. There was originally a systematic disagreement between the results obtained by the experimenters and de Broglie's theoretical value (5.1), but the explanation which removes the difficulty may be mentioned because it adds to the analogy between particle waves and optical waves.

Eckart and Bethe [1] have drawn attention to the necessity of considering the refractive index of the waves.

In calculating Bragg's formula (see below)

$$2d \sin \theta = n\lambda \qquad . \qquad . \qquad (5.2)$$

for X-rays, we assume that the refractive index of the crystal is unity, and this is the case for X-rays. If the index is μ the formula becomes

$$2d\sqrt{\mu^2 - \cos^2 \theta} = n\lambda \qquad . \qquad . \qquad (5.3)$$

We have seen in Chap. II (2.16) that the velocity of the wave is given by

$$U = \frac{h\nu}{\sqrt{2m(E - V)}} \qquad . \qquad . \qquad (5.4)$$

in a field where the potential energy is V, for example inside the crystal. Outside, where the field is zero,

$$U_0 = \frac{h\nu}{\sqrt{2mE}}.$$

Thus the refractive index is

$$\mu = \frac{U_0}{U} = \sqrt{\frac{E - V}{E}} \qquad . \qquad . \qquad (5.5)$$

In the experiments of Davisson and Germer E was of such a value that μ could have differed from unity in some

[1] *Naturwiss.*, **15**, 1927, p. 787.

cases by about $\frac{1}{10}$. In the experiments to be described below, where the electrons moved much more rapidly, the value of E is greater and μ does not differ from unity by an appreciable amount.

In the experiment just described the diffraction was caused by a single crystal. A very remarkable series of experiments has been carried out by G. P. Thomson in which the electron stream was directed upon a thin film composed of many small crystals.

The electrons were subjected to a fall of potential of the order of 25,000 volts. It is interesting to calculate the wave-length corresponding to this case, and the calculation will be made without entering into the refinement introduced by the relativity formula connecting mass and velocity.

Let m denote the mass of the electron, and v the velocity acquired in the field. Let P denote the potential difference in absolute units.

Thus
$$\tfrac{1}{2}mv^2 = eP \qquad (5.6)$$

whence
$$mv = \sqrt{2meP} \qquad (5.7)$$

and
$$\lambda = \frac{h}{\sqrt{2meP}} \qquad (5.8)$$

If the appropriate values be substituted, the wave-length obtained is 0.78×10^{-9} cm., or 0.078 Ångstroms. This is equal to the wave-length of very hard X-rays.

For voltages of the order of 100 such as those considered in the experiment described already, the wave-length is 1.22 Ångstroms. While Davisson and Germer's experiment is analogous to the single crystal experiments of Laue and Bragg, Thomson's experiment is analogous to that associated with the names of Debye, Hull and Scherrer, in which X-rays were reflected at the surfaces of small crystals arranged at random. The resulting pattern on a photographic plate shows a definite symmetry if certain crystal directions predominate.

Thomson caused a beam of cathode rays, made approximately homogeneous, to pass normally through a very

thin film. The rays were then received on a photographic
plate and the pattern studied.

The apparatus is of a simple character, the rays being
generated by the potential from an induction coil and caused
to pass through a fine tube, then through the film, to be
intercepted by a plate after travelling a distance of about
32·5 cm.

On developing the plate a symmetrical pattern about a
central spot was observed similar to that observed with
X-rays.

In regarding this as evidence in favour of the presence of
mechanical waves, we must be convinced that particles

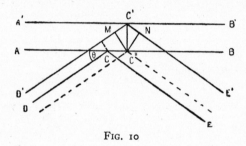

FIG. 10

strike the plate and produce the pattern and that the film
is essential.

It is conceivable that the cathode particles produce rays
and that these give the wave pattern, but this can be
decided by generating a magnetic field between the film
and plate. It was found that the pattern moved as a whole
under the influence of the field as if the beam arriving at
the plate consisted of charged particles all with the same
velocity. This differentiated the beam from one consisting
of rays such as X-rays, and it was also a test for the homo-
geneity of the beam.

With regard to the other point, it need only be stated
that on removing the film only the central spot appeared
on the plate and no pattern.

The first striking thing about this experiment is the qualitative agreement with the theory.

To appreciate the quantitative agreement we must turn to Bragg's theory of crystal reflection. According to this theory a crystal consists of atoms arranged in a definite way, each atom forming a centre at which the rays are scattered; from this it follows that we may regard a crystal as made up of planes oriented in certain directions. These planes pass through the atoms, and on account of the symmetry in the crystal structure, sets of parallel planes corresponding to the different layers of atoms occur; for example, if we think of the atoms arranged at the corners of a cube the planes will correspond to the sides and diagonal planes.

Let AB and $A'B'$ denote two consecutive parallel planes, and let two rays be incident at C and C' and leave along CE and $C'E'$. If these rays are in the same phase they will reinforce one another and produce an intense line on a photographic plate placed to receive them.

The difference in path between them is the same as that between the dotted path and the second ray. Let $C''M$ and $C''N$ be drawn perpendicularly to $C'D'$ and $C'E'$ respectively. The path difference is $MC' + C'N$. If θ denote the angle between the rays and the planes, and d the distance between the planes, this difference is equal to $2d \sin \theta$.

Thus the condition for reinforcement is

$$2d \sin \theta = n\lambda, \quad (n = 1, 2, 3, \ldots) \qquad . \quad (5.9)$$

the value of d differs according to the planes considered.

In the case of a cubic arrangement it is easy to express d in terms of the side of the cube, say a. Suppose that three directions parallel to the sides of the cubes are taken as axes, then the equation of a plane referred to these may be written : $lx + my + nz = p$, where (l, m, n) denote the direction cosines of the normal to the plane and p is the perpendicular from the origin on to the plane.

Let a plane through the origin be one of the diffracting planes with an adjacent parallel plane at distance d.

The equation for the adjacent plane is $lx + my + nz = d$,

and the plane can be denoted by the set of direction cosines (l, m, n). Instead of this three integers (h_1, h_2, h_3) are used to distinguish the plane by speaking of it as the "$h_1 h_2 h_3$ plane" where its equation is thrown into the form

$$h_1 x + h_2 y + h_3 z = a.$$

We have, of course,

$$\frac{h_1}{l} = \frac{h_2}{m} = \frac{h_3}{n} = \frac{a}{d},$$

and since $l^2 + m^2 + n^2 = 1$

$$d = \frac{a}{\sqrt{h_1{}^2 + h_2{}^2 + h_3{}^2}} \quad . \quad . \quad (5.10)$$

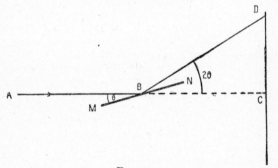

FIG. 11

which gives d in terms of a from the plane indices $(h_1 h_2 h_3)$.

Suppose that a thin film containing small crystals in all possible orientations at random receives a beam of X-rays, then by (5.9) we have reinforcement if

$$2d \sin \theta = n\lambda,$$

where d is the separation of the planes concerned and θ is the glancing angle on a small crystal.

If the reflected beam is received at D on a photographic plate and the angle is small, we have

$$CD = 2L\theta,$$

where C is the point of incidence of the primary on the plate in the absence of the crystal MN and L is the distance BC, i.e. the distance from film to plate.

Thus from (5.9) an intense spot lies at D if

$$CD = \frac{n\lambda L}{d}. \quad . \quad . \quad . \quad (5.11)$$

If B is the apex of a cone with its base to the right of the diagram, and if crystals lie so that the planes MN are tangent to the cone at the apex, a small pencil of rays along AB will fall at the same angle on all the crystal planes giving rise to a circle on the plate of radius CD. Since we assume that the crystals are arranged at random we have the equivalent of this diffracting cone.

For the same value of d we shall get a series of circles corresponding to the values of n. Other circles will be obtained for different planes MN, i.e. with different values of d, and it is possible that reflecting planes will occur in the crystal not much inclined to MN at which this diffraction can occur, the different values of θ required occurring in the beam AB, which cannot be quite parallel in practice.

If the arrangement is not at random the circles may be incomplete, and at any rate will show different intensities at different parts of the ring.

In order to put the theory to the test by verifying the equation (5.1), we have to measure the diameters of the rings formed, determine the planes responsible for the diffraction and deduce λ from (5.11). The experimental result can then be compared with the theoretical value.

The method used by Thomson was essentially this, but he made the test by calculating the constant a from the mechanical wave-length of the cathode rays and comparing this with the value determined in experiments on crystal structure.

It is interesting and instructive to refer to the original paper on this work for the photographs of the patterns obtained. One of these is for a gold film and the rings are remarkably clear and uniform in intensity. The diameters of these rings are approximately in the ratio 1 : 1·18 : 1·62 :

1·96.   We have to determine if the structure of gold crystals is such that planes occur which would produce rings with diameters in these ratios.   Gold crystals are built up as a face-centred cubic lattice and for the sake of simplicity we take three planes with indices $(2, 0, 0)$, $(2, 2, 0)$ and $(1, 1, 3)$ and find the ratios of the diameters to be expected.   If we refer to (5.11) and consider the first order ring ($n = 1$) the ratios are inversely as the corresponding values of d, and that according to (5.10) is in the ratio of the corresponding values of $\sqrt{h_1{}^2 + h_2{}^2 + h_3{}^2}$ so that in this case the ratios are

$$\sqrt{4} : \sqrt{8} : \sqrt{11}$$
$$= 2 : 2\cdot83 : 3\cdot32$$
$$= 1 : 1\cdot41 : 1\cdot66.$$

We may write the ratios of the last three observed rings, given above, as

$$1 : 1\cdot39 : 1\cdot66$$

so that we may claim that these observed rings are accounted for.   By examination of other planes it was found possible to account for the first ring.

A film of aluminium gave equally convincing evidence.

Another striking quantitative result can be obtained by observing that if D denote the diameter of a ring on the pattern $\dfrac{D}{\lambda}$ should be constant for the same order n (5.11).

Thus by varying λ and observing the value of D we can test this result.

There is no point in making a relativity correction here so that we may use the value given above, viz. :

$$\lambda = \frac{h}{\sqrt{2mPe}},$$

which shows that the theory anticipates that $D\sqrt{P}$ is a constant.   Thus by measuring P, the potential applied to the cathode rays, by varying it and measuring the diameters it is easy to test the result.

A very good agreement was found, as will be seen by reference to the original paper where the results are given for aluminium and gold. The agreement here is strong evidence in favour of the wave-like behaviour of the electrons.

With regard to the determination of the value of a by this experiment, the X-ray value for gold is 4.065×10^{-8} cm., and the value obtained is within about 1 per cent. of this.

Experiments of the same kind as the foregoing have been carried out by many workers with the result that the law of wave-length has now been firmly established and has become known as the de Broglie law.

The experiments of M. Ponte,[1] though based on the same principle as that of the Debye-Scherrer experiment, must be mentioned because of the great improvement in a point of technique.

The method of G. P. Thomson requires the deposition of a thin crystallised film, and requires a delicate and difficult technique.

In Ponte's experiments crystalline powders of zinc, magnesium and cadmium oxides were used. A narrow beam of electrons from a hot cathode was directed on to a thin metallic wire or on the edge of a diaphragm on which the oxide had been formed. The beam was thus not required to pass through the film, and the very delicate deposition of a thin film was not necessary.

In this way, by using tensions varying between 7.6 and 17.25 kilovolts as many as 20 rings were determined and crystal dimensions calculated. The results obtained agree within 1 per cent. with those of Bragg.

The Application of Electronic Diffraction to the Study of Surface Phenomena.

—The phenomena occurring in the diffraction of slow electrons open new possibilities for the examination of surface structure. They have the advantage that they penetrate less deeply than

---

[1] *Comptes Rendus*, 1928, **188,** p. 244.

X-rays. In the case of electrons only the first ten or twenty planes are involved, while in the case of X-rays a thousand and more come into consideration.

The electronic interaction with the atoms shows itself by the occurrence of a refractive index for slow electrons.

In Davisson and Germer's experiment there occurred certain characteristics in the diffraction pattern which were attributed to several layers of gas atoms at the crystal surface.

The investigation of these layers has been carried out in later work by Germer and Rupp.[1]

The effect of allowing gas to come into contact with a nickel surface in Davisson and Germer's experiment was to diminish the intensity of the diffraction maxima, and this was due to layers of gas molecules covering the surface.

In addition to this intensity change, two other types of diffraction pattern were observed These appeared after heating a crystal and allowing it to cool. They were of short duration and were noticeable a short time after the heating process.

Germer has plotted on a graph a series of values of the wave-length against sin θ. (θ is the angle of diffraction.) For a diffraction pattern the relation should be linear. He has found that from the nickel itself lines occur corresponding to the orders $n = 1, 2, 3$, while the diffraction pattern of one of the two types above-mentioned corresponds to the order $\frac{1}{2}$. We have in this case to do with a plane grating with an element of double the magnitude of that responsible for the other orders.

Germer has concluded that the gas atoms form a single layer arranged like the atoms of the crystal, but with a double separation, and situated at a depth of 3 Å below the first layer of nickel atoms.

The arrangement is illustrated in Fig. 12.

In Rupp's experiments a stream of electrons was allowed

<hr />

[1] Germer (*Z. f. Ph.*, 1929, **54**, p. 408). Rupp (*A. d. Ph.*, 1930, **5**, p. 453).

to fall on a nickel surface and the potential driving them varied. The electrons fell into a metal receiver after

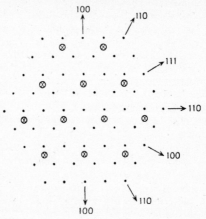

FIG. 12.—Arrangement of absorbed gas atoms at the surface of a Ni crystal. ● Ni atoms. ⊗ Gas atoms.

reflection, and the intensities were measured corresponding to different wave-lengths, i.e. to different values of the potential V.

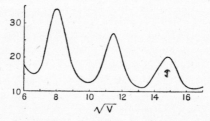

FIG. 13.—Pure nickel. Incidence at 10° on the (111) face.

Curves were plotted showing the variation of intensity with $\sqrt{V}$ as in Figs. 13 and 14.

The angle of incidence was maintained constant, and the receiver was placed so that the ray entering it left the crystal at an angle to the incident angle.   Fig. 13 shows that for voltages of 67, 132, 215, i.e. for certain values of λ, the intensity attains maximum values.   The corresponding orders are 3, 4 and 5.

After obtaining the pure nickel curve hydrogen was allowed to enter the tube.   It remained in contact with the metal for about ten minutes at a pressure of 10^{-4} mm. Hg and was then pumped off.

About half an hour after the entrance of hydrogen the electron reflection was measured, beginning with low and

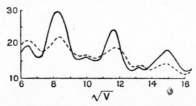

FIG. 14.—Continuous curve H_2 on nickel at 10^{-4} mm. Hg.   Dotted curve, H_2 on nickel, two days later.

passing the high electronic velocities in order not to disturb the gas layer.

The new curve is the continuous curve of Fig. 14.   The main nickel maxima remain, but new ones have put in their appearance as subsidiary maxima.   These new maxima are situated at points corresponding to voltages of 41, 96, 170, and the orders are $2\frac{1}{2}$, $3\frac{1}{2}$ and $4\frac{1}{2}$.

The dotted curve, taken two days later, shows a change in the intensities in the nickel maxima, and it is thought that this is due to the fact that the gas layer has become less regular, but the experiment gives no detailed information on this point, and Rupp describes the process as " surface loosening ".

Various substances were investigated in the same way, argon on nickel, hydrogen on copper, etc.

Diffraction of Electrons by a Ruled Grating.—The fact that electrons and X-rays are diffracted in the same way by crystals suggests that there may be a similarity in the case of diffraction by a ruled grating.

The possibility of carrying out experiments of this kind has been examined by Rupp[1] and Worsnop.[2] The following is an account of Rupp's experiment, which again verified the existence of electronic wave properties, the wave-length being given by de Broglie's formula.

Fig. 15 illustrates the apparatus diagrammatically. A tungsten wire covered with barium oxide was placed at K and between this wire and a second wire L there was a

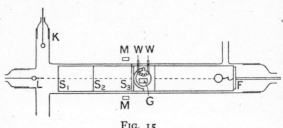

FIG. 15

tension of about 12 volts. From the second wire to the shutter S_1 the chief potential drop was maintained, and it could be varied.

In this way the film was protected from direct light from the hot wire.

S_1, S_2 and S_3 denote three shutters, and the magnetic coil MM focused electrons from S_1 on the film at F.

Beyond S_3 the electrons struck the grating G, which could be rotated and set at an angle to the axis by means of a micrometer screw.

The coil WW represents a tungsten spiral for bombardment of the grating.

[1] *Zeit. f. Phys.*, **52**, p. 8.
[2] *Proc. Phys. Soc.*, xxxvi, p. 284. *Nature*, Feb. 2, 1920.

The distance S_1S_2 was 32 cm., and from the grating to the film 38·5 cm. Let an incident ray S_1G strike the grating at the grazing angle θ, and let GF_1 denote the reflected ray. Let GF_2 denote a diffracted ray, making an angle α with GF_1.

If we apply the diffraction grating formula to this case, bearing in mind that the angles are small, we find

$$\tfrac{1}{2}d\alpha(\alpha + 2\theta) = n\lambda,$$

where d is the grating constant.

In the grating employed by Rupp $d = 7\cdot70 \times 10^{-4}$ cm. measured by means of the mercury green line.

The experimental results may be examined in two ways. The first is a relative method, and consists in maintaining

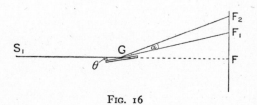

Fig. 16

constant, while the electronic velocity is varied. From the experiment the value of θ may be deduced for each velocity, i.e. each λ, and the results should agree in all the cases. The experiment gives α and $\lambda = \dfrac{h}{mv}$, so that θ may be calculated from the above formula.

The second is an absolute method. It consists in observing the different orders in the diffraction pattern and the corresponding angles of diffraction. From these observations both θ and λ can be calculated.

The reason for this procedure is that the grazing angle is not able to be measured with the necessary accuracy. According to Rupp, the experimental results verified the theory to an accuracy of about 2 per cent.

Experiments of Neutral Particles.—In searching for another opportunity to test the de Broglie wave-length relation, it is natural to examine the possibility of making use of gaseous molecules. In this case the mass of the particle is large, but the velocity is comparatively small. The value of the wave-length in the case of hydrogen at room temperature is approximately 10^{-8} cm. for the molecules moving with the most probable velocity.

T. H. Johnson [1] investigated the reflection of atoms by crystals, using a plate smoked with molybdenum trioxide as a detector. This substance becomes blackened where hydrogen atoms strike it. The results indicate that the atoms have a wave-like character.

Ellett, Olson and Zahl [2] have made experiments with

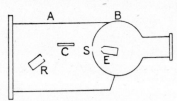

Fig. 17.—Diagram to illustrate the apparatus of Stern and Estermann.

mercury, cadmium and arsenic beams, which they caused to fall on a rock-salt surface.

They conclude from their results that the reflection is of the type associated with the name of Bragg in the case of X-rays. They have shown that a beam reflected by a crystal acquires a property by virtue of which it is entirely reflected by a second crystal when the second angle of incidence is equal to the first. The beam is in some way prepared by the first crystal for this particular type of reflection by the second.

They have also shown that the reflected beam is made up

[1] *Jour. Franklin Inst.*, 1928, **206**, p. 301.
[2] *Phys. Rev.*, 1929, **34**, 405.

of atoms all with very nearly the same velocity, which varies with the angle of reflection, and that the intensity of the reflected beam also varies with the angle of reflection.

In these experiments the reflected atoms are detected by receiving them on a glass surface cooled by liquid air.

Stern, Knauer and Estermann have conducted a series of experiments on the diffraction of gas molecules, and we shall give a short account of experiments described in one of their papers.[1] The apparatus consisted of two main chambers A and B, separated by a partition carrying a slit S. The apparatus is represented diagrammatically in Fig. 17. E is an ejector from which the molecules are shot through the slit on to the crystal C, and R is a receiver which can be adjusted to receive the molecules as they come from the crystal.

The pressure in chamber A was of the order of 10^{-5} mm. Hg, and in B of the order 10^{-4} mm. Hg. These pressures were recorded by a Macleod gauge.

The receiver was connected to a manometer which measured the changes in pressure due to the incidence of the beam of molecules. This manometer is a very important part of the apparatus, and it must be sufficiently sensitive to determine changes of pressure of the order 10^{-8} mm. Hg. The pressure prevailing is of the order 10^{-5} mm. Hg.

The experimenters finally decided upon the Pirani hot-wire manometer as being the most suitable instrument, and they describe some improvements for the increase in the sensitivity of the instrument.

The gases used were hydrogen and helium, and the velocity of ejection from E was controlled by means of the temperature.

The distribution of velocities is known from the Maxwellian law, and this can be translated into a distribution among wave-lengths by applying de Broglie's relation.

---

[1] *Zeit. f. Phys.*, 1930, **61**, p. 95.

It can be shown that the wave-length of greatest intensity is given by

$$\lambda_m = 19\cdot47 \times 10^{-8} \times \frac{1}{\sqrt{Tm}} \text{ cm.,}$$

where T denotes the absolute temperature and m the mass of a molecule. It seems impossible to think of the process as one of diffraction at a space grating, since the molecules cannot penetrate the crystal. We must regard the phenomenon as one of diffraction at a surface if it is diffraction at all.

Let the z-axis lie perpendicularly to the crystal surface, and let the x- and y-axes lie along the two principal axes

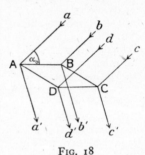

FIG. 18

of the grating. Consider a beam of parallel rays falling upon a grating, one element of which is represented in Fig. 18 by $ABCD$.

Imagine a wave-front drawn at right angles to the bundle of rays aA, bB, cC and dD, and a second wave-front at right angles to Aa', Bb', Cc' and Dd'.

The paths of aAa' and bBb' between these wave-fronts differ by $(\cos \alpha - \cos \alpha_0)\, AB$, where α_0 and α are the angles made by the incident and diffracted rays with AB.

Similarly, the path difference for the rays cCc' and bBb' is $(\cos \beta - \cos \beta_0)BC$, where β_0 and β are the angles made with BC.

In any direction in which these path differences amount

to a whole number of wave-lengths we shall find reinforcement of vibrations, and thus the diffraction pattern is determined by the equations

$$\cos \alpha - \cos \alpha_0 = h_1 \frac{\lambda}{d}$$

$$\cos \beta - \cos \beta_0 = h_2 \frac{\lambda}{d},$$

where h_1 and h_2 are integers (positive or negative), λ is the wave-length of the incident waves, and d the grating element, supposed the same in both directions, i.e.

$$AB = BC = d.$$

The orders of the diffracted rays are described by means of the integers, e.g. (h_1, h_2).

In the experiments of Stern and Estermann, the ray was generally incident in the xz-plane, so that β_0 had the value 90°.

If the values of h_1 and h_2 are both zero, $\alpha = \alpha_0$ and $\beta = 90°$. This corresponds to the reflected ray. In the experiment the diffracted rays of order $(0, \pm 1)$ were observed as well.

The diagram shows the result for the case of rays formed of helium molecules incident upon a crystal of lithium fluoride at an angle of $11\frac{1}{2}°$ and at the temperature of 22° C.

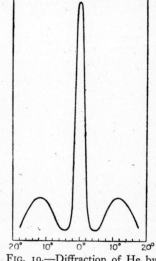

Fig. 19.—Diffraction of He by LiF.

The process consisted in directing rays at a constant angle of incidence upon the crystal and setting the receiver at an equal angle to the normal to the crystal surface.

The abscissa zero of the diagram corresponds to the case where the receiver lies in the plane of incidence.

By rotation of the receiver about the normal into different azimuths variations of pressure were detected. The abscissæ measure the azimuths and the ordinates are proportional to the manometer readings, i.e. to the ray intensities in the different directions.

Two subsidiary maxima occur on either side of the zero in azimuths of approximately 12°. The positions of the calculated maxima for the orders $(0, \pm 1)$ are at $11\frac{3}{4}°$. The agreement is very good.

This curve is typical of many obtained, and recorded in the original paper.

Neutrons.—In a study of the diffraction of neutrons by a single crystal W. H. Zinn [1] obtained a striking confirmation of the validity of de Broglie's wave-length relation in

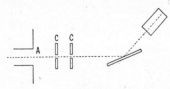

FIG. 20

the case of neutrons. Neutrons from a chain reacting pile entered a large block of graphite which reduced the average velocity to the equilibrium value for graphite at room temperature. The wave-length associated with neutrons of this velocity is of the order of that of X-rays so that diffraction experiments with crystals are suggested as a means of examining the wave-like characteristic of these particles.

The neutrons from the pile leave it at A and are collimated by cadmium slits at CC. The collimated beam

[1] *Phys. Rev.*, 1947, **71**, p. 752.

falls on the (100) plane of a single calcite crystal and the diffracted neutrons are detected by a boron trifluoride counter.

The velocity of the neutrons was measured and the reciprocal of the speed plotted against the sine of the glancing angle, θ. The points plotted on the graph were found to lie on the line

$$\frac{h}{mv} = 2d \sin \theta,$$

where h is Planck's constant and m the mass of the neutron.

CHAPTER VI

THE FIRST ORDER EQUATION OF THE QUANTUM THEORY

WHEN the lines of the hydrogen spectrum are examined by an instrument of high resolving power they are found to be multiple. The formula (4.25) for the energy corresponding to the various levels which results from the theory of Bohr and Sommerfeld and also from that of Schrödinger is thus unsatisfactory, for it suggests that transitions take place between levels which have single values and that the corresponding lines are single.

Sommerfeld was able to account for fine structure by applying the mechanics of the theory of relativity to the study of the orbital motion of the electron. The classical treatment was modified by replacing the constant mass of the particle by the relativistic value dependent upon the velocity. The orbits according to this theory then approximate to ellipses which rotate in their plane.

The effect on the energy value is that it depends not simply upon the total quantum number n of formula (4.25) but also upon the azimuthal quantum number k, where $k = l + 1$ (*cf.* equation 4.21).

The value of the energy to a close approximation is

$$E = -\frac{2\pi^2 m e^4}{h^2 n^2} - \frac{m c^2 \alpha^4}{2n^4}\left(\frac{n}{k} - \frac{3}{4}\right), \qquad . \quad (6.1)$$

where $\alpha = 2\pi e^2/hc$.

In this formula k can take the integral values from 1 to n so that the single levels of the earlier theory become n in number with slightly differing energy values.

The Balmer line H_α results from transitions between the levels $n = 3$ and $n = 2$ and, if it be remembered that the permitted transitions are between levels for which k

changes by $\pm$ 1, it appears that three lines should be observed. This appeared at first to be in agreement with experiment in the case of hydrogen but in the case of ionized helium, to which the theory ought also to apply, where the line separation is greater and thus more easily observed, it was seen that the number of lines was incorrectly given. Sommerfeld's formula, however, is quantitatively correct for the separations of the lines for which it accounts. In the case of hydrogen the lines are very close together and difficult to separate but a careful examination shows that the number of lines is greater than the three derived from Sommerfeld's formula.

Later on the study of the spectra of the alkalis revealed a difficulty. In this case the outermost electron of the atom moves in the electric field resulting from the nucleus and the remaining electrons. The effect is that the electron describes a rotating orbit not unlike that of the relativistic orbit of the hydrogen electron. The energy of the outer electron depends on the azimuthal quantum number as well as upon the total quantum number. The relativistic effect in this case is small in comparison with that due to the electric field. It was found, however, that the energy levels for given values of n and k were double. This doubling of the levels thus differs from the multiplicity due to the relativistic effect for this is attributed to differing values of k.

This difficulty concerning the alkali doublets was pointed out by Millikan and Bowen[1] and also by Lande,[2] and not long afterwards an explanation came from the introduction of the concept of electron spin by Goudsmit and Uhlenbeck.[3] At this time it appeared that in the case of the hydrogen atom the fine structure could be accounted for by the relativity effect while the alkali doublet structure showed that it was necessary to attribute a spin to the electron. The problem was to explain the neglect of spin in deriving Sommerfeld's formula.

[1] *Phys. Rev.*, 1924, **24**, p. 223.   [2] *Ibid.*, **25**, p. 46.
[3] *Naturwiss*, 1925, **13**, p. 953.

An explanation came from work by Heisenberg and Jordan [1] who, by the use of the principles of quantum mechanics, calculated the energy of the electron of the hydrogen atom taking account both of the spin and relativity effects. They showed that in addition to the Balmer formula for the energy of a level the two effects together give an additional energy term of magnitude

$$\frac{mc^2\alpha^4}{2n^4}\left(\frac{n}{j+\frac{1}{2}} - \frac{3}{4}\right). \qquad . \qquad . \quad (6.2)$$

If this be compared with Sommerfeld's formula (6.1) a similarity of form in the two expressions is observed but the important difference is that (6.2) depends on the inner quantum number j and not upon the azimuthal quantum number k or, in the notation now adopted, not upon $l \; (= k - 1)$.

The application of this formula and the selection rule for j will be considered later in this chapter.

In spite of the success in overcoming some difficulties associated with the older theory the form of the fundamental equation of the quantum theory is not satisfactory, for Schrödinger's equation is not in a form compatible with the principle of relativity. In addition, it is not possible to derive from it the correct energy formula to account for fine structure.

Sommerfeld's treatment of the relativistic motion of the electron in its orbit in the hydrogen atom suggests that in order to account for fine structure it is necessary to introduce the relativistic values of energy and momentum into Schrödinger's equation, that is to say, to begin with equation (2.15) instead of (2.13). But, if this is done, although a formula like that of Sommerfeld is obtained the energy values are incorrect.

The incompatibility of Schrödinger's equation with the principle of relativity is evident from its form in (2.18).

According to this principle the co-ordinates of space and time should occur in the same way but in the equation the differential operators with respect to x, y, z are of the second degree while $\dfrac{\partial}{\partial t}$ occurs in the first.

The idea occurred to Dirac that the fundamental equation of quantum mechanics should be of the first degree and should satisfy the principle of special relativity.

In Schrödinger's equation in the form (2.13) the operator

$$H = \frac{1}{2m_0} \sum \left(\frac{h}{2\pi i} \frac{\partial}{\partial x} \right)^2 + V . \qquad (6.3)$$

takes the place of the expression $(T + V)$ which represents the total energy, for (2.13) can be written in the form

$$H\psi = E\psi, \text{ (p. 30)}.$$

If E be replaced by the operator $-\dfrac{h}{2\pi i}.\dfrac{\partial}{\partial t}$, the relation

$$-\frac{h}{2\pi i}.\frac{\partial \psi}{\partial t} = H\psi . \qquad (6.4)$$

is identical with (2.18).

H is described in quantum mechanics as the Hamiltonian operator.

In Dirac's theory the Hamiltonian, which will also be denoted by H, is of the first order in the operators $\dfrac{\partial}{\partial x}$, etc.

It will be seen that Dirac's theory leads to energy values for the electron of the hydrogen atom which are identical with the formula obtained from the considerations of the relativistic and spin effects. But Dirac set out to satisfy the requirements of relativity and, without further hypothesis, obtained the energy formula. The terms previously described as relativistic and spin terms are combined in the theory, which reveals a union between the two effects not suggested by any previous ideas.

Dirac's equation is fundamental in mechanical theories and takes a place to be compared with that occupied by the fundamental equations of classical mechanics. From one point of view it occupies a place in the theory of small scale phenomena analogous to that of Einstein's law of gravitation in the theory of relativity.

Notation.—In order to carry out his object Dirac introduced certain quantities which had not previously had much application in physics. These are known as matrices and in order to appreciate the theory, it is necessary to learn something of their character and properties.

A matrix is represented by a symbol, say A, as follows :

$$A = \begin{vmatrix} A_{11} & A_{12} & A_{13} & A_{14} \\ A_{21} & A_{22} & A_{23} & A_{24} \\ A_{31} & A_{32} & A_{33} & A_{34} \\ A_{41} & A_{42} & A_{43} & A_{44} \end{vmatrix} = \begin{vmatrix} A_{mn} \end{vmatrix}$$

The quantities A_{11}, etc., are described as elements of the matrix and are denoted typically by A_{mn}.

The number of rows and columns is not necessarily four but the matrices of Dirac's equation have this number of rows and columns and are described as four-rowed matrices.

A matrix is an operator and occurs in association with some other quantity upon which it acts according to the rules of matrix calculus. In this respect it is similar to a differential operator associated with a function in differentiation, e.g. $\frac{d}{dx}$ operating on F to give $\frac{dF}{dx}$.

The operation which occurs most frequently in quantum mechanics is that of multiplication and it is the only one which need be introduced for the present purpose. Two matrices A and B when multiplied give a matrix C with components C_{mn} derived as follows :

$$C_{mn} = \sum_p A_{mp} B_{pn}, \qquad . \qquad . \qquad (6.5)$$

the summation being taken over p, which in four-rowed matrices takes the values 1 to 4.

The sign of summation will be dropped with the understanding that when a suffix occurs twice in an expression such as $A_{mp} B_{pn}$ it is to be summed.

It will be noted that the order of the factors is of importance, for $A_{mp}B_{pn}$ is not in general equal to $B_{mp}A_{pn}$.

This is expressed by writing $A \cdot B \neq B \cdot A$, the dot between the factors denoting multiplication in the way defined. When it happens that $A \cdot B = B \cdot A$, the matrices A and B are said to commute.

Matrices in the quantum theory may have complex elements. The matrix which has elements which are the complex conjugates of A is denoted by A^* and thus

$$A^* = \mid A^*_{mn} \mid.$$

Another matrix associated with A is known as its adjoint $A^\dagger$ which is formed with elements $A^\dagger_{mn} = A_{nm}^*$. An important case is that of matrices in which $A = A^\dagger$.

A single column matrix occurs in the quantum theory, denoted by ψ. It has only four components differing from zero. These are the components $\psi_{11}, \psi_{21}, \psi_{31}, \psi_{41}$, and the fact that the second suffix is unity in each case leads to its omission and the components are denoted by $\psi_1, \psi_2, \psi_3, \psi_4$. This gives the quantity the appearance of a four-vector but it is not a quantity of this type and does not satisfy the relativistic transformation rule for a four-vector. Its conjugate has four components of which ψ_n^* is typical. The adjoint of ψ is $\psi^\dagger$ with components $\psi^\dagger_{mn} = \psi^*_{nm}$ so that since m can have only the value unity $\psi^\dagger$ has four components $(\psi^*_1, \psi^*_2, \psi^*_3, \psi^*_4)$ and it is a matrix with only one row.

In Dirac's theory Schrödinger's wave function ψ, which is a scalar quantity, is replaced by the new ψ with these four components and the square of ψ or $\psi\psi^*$ now becomes

$$\psi^*\psi = \psi_n^*\psi_n.$$

The matrices occurring in Dirac's theory are of a comparatively simple type. They are four in number and they can be represented by a single table as follows :

$$\alpha = \begin{vmatrix} u & 0 & z & x - iy \\ 0 & u & x + iy & -z \\ z & x - iy & -u & 0 \\ x + iy & -z & 0 & -u \end{vmatrix} \quad (6.6)$$

By writing $x = 1$ and $y = z = u = 0$, the matrix α_x (or α_1) is obtained. By writing $y = 1, x = z = u = 0$, α_y (or α_2) is obtained and so on, the fourth is usually denoted by β.

To these must be added the unit matrix:

$$I = \begin{vmatrix} 1 & 0 & 0 & 0 \\ 0 & 1 & 0 & 0 \\ 0 & 0 & 1 & 0 \\ 0 & 0 & 0 & 1 \end{vmatrix},$$

which has the property of leaving unchanged any quantity which it multiplies.

Thus $\qquad IA = AI = A.$

By making use of the multiplication rule (6.5) it will be found that the squares of the four matrices are equal to the unit matrix.

It will also be found that the different matrices are non-commutative and that, in fact,

$$\alpha_x\alpha_y + \alpha_y\alpha_x = 0.$$

These results can be expressed by the formula

$$\alpha_m\alpha_n + \alpha_n\alpha_m = 2\delta_{mn} \qquad . \qquad . \qquad (6.7)$$

for the four values of m and n. δ_{mn} is unity when $m = n$, otherwise it is zero.

It is helpful to compare these Dirac matrices with the fundamental vectors (i, j, k) of three dimensional vector analysis. Certain quantities and operators can be expressed in terms of these unit orthogonal vectors.

The familiar properties of these vectors are

$$i^2 = j^2 = k^2 = 1$$
$$i \cdot j = j \cdot k = k \cdot i = 0$$

and these relations correspond to those of (6.7).

A vector A can be expressed in the form

$$A = iA_x + jA_y + kA_z$$

and the gradient operator by

$$\nabla = i\frac{\partial}{\partial x} + j\frac{\partial}{\partial y} + k\frac{\partial}{\partial z}.$$

In matrix analysis an operator A is often expressed in the form

$$A = \alpha_m A_m, \qquad . \qquad . \qquad . \qquad (6.8)$$

where the summation is over values of $m = 1, 2, 3, 4$ and A_m is an ordinary quantity.

An important operator in quantum mechanics is

$$\alpha_k \frac{\partial}{\partial x^k} + \frac{2\pi i m_0 c}{h} \beta, \qquad . \qquad . \qquad (6.9)$$

where k is summed from 1 to 3 and β (or α_4) is the fourth matrix.

As an example of (6.8) if $A_m = dx_m$ a matrix length ds is obtained,

$$ds = \alpha_1 dx_1 + \alpha_2 dx_2 + \alpha_3 dx_3 = \alpha_k dx_k$$

taking the first 3 matrices only.

$$(ds)^2 = (\alpha_k dx_k)^2 = (\alpha_k dx_k)(\alpha_l dx_l) = \alpha_k \alpha_l dx_k dx_l.$$

This expression contains such terms as

$$(\alpha_1)^2 (dx_1)^2 + (\alpha_1 \alpha_2 + \alpha_2 \alpha_1) dx_1 dx_2$$

so that according to the expression (6.7)

$$ds^2 = \Sigma dx_n^2.$$

The quantity on the right has lost the appearance of a matrix although it must be remembered that it is strictly to be multiplied by the unit matrix.

The operator ds is said to have the characteristic or proper value of the square root of Σdx_n^2. This is evidently the distance between two points separated by displacements (dx_n). The suggestion is that representation by matrices is more fundamental than ordinary representation and that the quantities which are familiar in the ordinary calculus of physics are proper values. The link between the matrix and the ordinary calculus is thus by means of the relations (6.7).

It has already been stated (p. 91) that in Dirac's equation $\frac{\partial}{\partial x}$, etc., occur linearly and (p. 93) that the scalar function ψ is replaced by a single column matrix (ψ_n).

The comparison between Schrödinger's equation and the energy relation of ordinary mechanics has been pointed out (p. 30), and in passing to the more general form of the equation (2.18) in addition to the substitution of operators for components of momentum the substitution of the energy W by $-\frac{h}{2\pi i}\frac{\partial}{\partial t}$ has been made.

The question arises whether a linear relation exists between the components of momentum and the energy which could be converted to an equation in the matrix ψ by the substitution of the appropriate differential operators.

The representation of a matrix quantity in (6.8) and the application to the line element offers a clue.

Let p_x, p_y, p_z denote the components of momentum of a free particle. The relation

$$\frac{W^2}{c^2} = p_x{}^2 + p_y{}^2 + p_z{}^2 + m_0{}^2 c^2 \quad . \quad (6.10)$$

is familiar in the mechanics of the special theory of relativity, where W denotes the kinetic energy of the particle, $W = mc^2$. The relation reduces to the formula for mass as a function of velocity

$$m = m_0 / \sqrt{1 - v^2/c^2}.$$

The quantity on the right hand side of equation (6.10) suggests the consideration of the matrix quantity

$$A = \alpha_x p_x + \alpha_y p_y + \alpha_z p_z + \beta m_0 c, \quad . \quad (6.11)$$

and from the properties of the matrices it follows that

$$A^2 = p_x{}^2 + p_y{}^2 + p_z{}^2 + m_0{}^2 c^2.$$

Thus the suggestion is that $A = W/c$, where W now becomes the operator

$$W = c(\alpha_x p_x + \alpha_y p_y + \alpha_z p_z + \beta m_0 c) \quad . \quad (6.12)$$

Replacing W, p_x, etc., by the appropriate operators the following operator results :

$$-\frac{h}{2\pi i}\frac{\partial}{\partial t} = c\left(\alpha_x \frac{h}{2\pi i}\cdot\frac{\partial}{\partial x} + \alpha_y \frac{h}{2\pi i}\cdot\frac{\partial}{\partial y} + \alpha_z \frac{h}{2\pi i}\frac{\partial}{\partial z} + \beta m_0 c\right)$$

If this is now allowed to act upon a quantity ψ with four components (ψ_n) the equation

$$\frac{h}{2\pi i}\frac{\partial\psi}{\partial t} + c\left(\alpha_x \frac{h}{2\pi i}\cdot\frac{\partial\psi}{\partial x} + . + . . + \beta m_0 c\psi\right) = 0 \quad (6.13)$$

is obtained.

This equation is of the form required by the theory of relativity and is in close analogy with the energy equation of a free particle in mechanics. Thus the operator

$$H = c(\alpha_x P_x + \alpha_y P_y + \alpha_z P_z + \beta m_0 c) \quad . \quad (6.14)$$

is described as the Hamiltonian operator of quantum mechanics, where for simplicity the P's denote the differential operators : $\frac{h}{2\pi i}\cdot\frac{\partial}{\partial x}$, etc.

Equation (6.13) is Dirac's equation for a free particle and in order to become familiar with the notation the operations concerned in this expression are considered in some detail.

The introduction of ψ as a matrix may be regarded as a necessary consequence of the introduction of the matrices α and β into the fundamental equation. It might have been necessary to introduce ψ as a four-rowed matrix but in the representation of the electron the simpler form is sufficient. In the equation the α's, β and ψ are multiplied in accordance with the rule (6.5) which in this case becomes

$$(\alpha_x \psi)_m = (\alpha_x)_{mn}\psi_n. \quad . \quad . \quad (6.15)$$

Thus each product has four components and equation (6.13) embodies four equations corresponding to the values 1, 2, 3, 4 for m. The function ψ is subject to two operations in the equation, that of differentiation and that represented by (6.15).

The equation resulting from taking the first component of (6.13) taking $m = 1$ and making use of the elements of the matrices given in the table (6.6) is :

$$\frac{h}{2\pi i}\frac{\partial \psi_1}{\partial t} + c\left\{\frac{h}{2\pi i}\frac{\partial}{\partial x}(\alpha_x\psi)_1 + \frac{h}{2\pi i}\frac{\partial}{\partial y}(\alpha_y\psi)_1 + \frac{h}{2\pi i}\frac{\partial}{\partial z}(\alpha_z\psi)_1\right.$$
$$\left. + m_0 c(\beta\psi)_1\right\} = 0 \quad . \quad . \quad (6.16)$$

α_x, etc., being composed of constant elements.

It will be found that

$$(\alpha_x\psi)_1 = (\alpha_x)_{1n}\psi_n = \psi_4, \quad (\alpha_y\psi)_1 = -i\psi_4,$$
$$(\alpha_z\psi)_1 = \psi_3, \quad (\beta\psi)_1 = \psi_1.$$
$$\left(\frac{h}{2\pi i}\frac{\partial}{\partial t} + m_0 c^2\right)\psi_1 + c\left[\frac{h}{2\pi i}\left(\frac{\partial}{\partial x} - i\frac{\partial}{\partial y}\right)\psi_4\right]$$
$$+ c\frac{h}{2\pi i}\frac{\partial \psi_3}{\partial z} = 0.$$

As before let the operators $\frac{h}{2\pi i}\frac{\partial}{\partial x}$ be denoted by P_1, etc., and the momentum components by p_1, etc., and let $-\frac{h}{2\pi i}\frac{\partial}{\partial t}$ be denoted by H, the energy being denoted by W.

Thus the last equation can be written in the form :

$$\left.\begin{array}{l} (-H + m_0 c^2)\psi_1 + c(P_1 - iP_2)\psi_4 + cP_3\psi_3 = 0 \\ \text{Similarly for the other components of the equation} \\ (-H + m_0 c^2)\psi_2 + c(P_1 + iP_2)\psi_3 - cP_3\psi_4 = 0 \\ (-H - m_0 c^2)\psi_3 + c(P_1 - iP_2)\psi_2 + cP_3\psi_1 = 0 \\ (-H - m_0 c^2)\psi_4 + c(P_1 + iP_2)\psi_1 - cP_3\psi_2 = 0 \end{array}\right\} \quad (6.17)$$

Since the particle is free it will be represented by a simple wave function, the four quantities (ψ_n) being constant multiples of exp. $\frac{2\pi i}{h}(p_1 x + p_2 y + p_z z - Wt)$. Let these multiples be a_1, a_2, a_3 and a_4 respectively.

Since $P_1\psi_1 = p_1\psi_1$, etc., and $H\psi_1 = W\psi_1$, equations (6.17) give the following equations for the constants:

$$(-W + m_0c^2)a_1 + c(p_1 - ip_2)a_4 + cp_3a_3 = 0$$
$$(-W + m_0c^2)a_2 + c(p_1 + ip_2)a_3 - cp_3a_4 = 0$$
$$(-W - m_0c^2)a_3 + c(p_1 - ip_2)a_2 + cp_3a_1 = 0$$
$$(-W - m_0c^2)a_4 + c(p_1 + ip_2)a_1 - cp_3a_2 = 0.$$

If there are to be values of the a's which satisfy these equations and are different from zero, the determinant of the coefficients of the a's must vanish. This requires the relation

$$W^2 = c^2(p_1{}^2 + p_2{}^2 + p_3{}^2 + m_0{}^2c^2)$$

which means that $W^2 = m^2c^4$, where $m = m_0/\sqrt{1 - v^2/c^2}$. When this condition holds values of the constants different from zero can be obtained.

An interesting point is that the energy W has a negative as well as a positive value. It might be suggested that the negative value is inapplicable and should be disregarded as having no physical significance. This is a suggestion which can be adopted without difficulty in ordinary mechanics, but the functions determined by the wave equation are characteristic functions which can be used by superposition to represent a physical state of the particle or system described by the equation.

This procedure can be compared with the representation of the state of a vibrating string by means of a Fourier series in which all the principal modes of vibration are superposed. It is not legitimate to omit arbitrarily any mode of vibration from the series. If a term is not present in any particular case it is because the special circumstances cause the amplitude of the term to vanish.

In the case of the wave equation all the characteristic functions are significant for a similar reason.

If the wave theory is accepted the situation is not that certain terms are to be omitted but that an attempt must be made to understand their significance. It has to be realized that wave mechanics is fundamentally different from ordinary mechanics, although in some cases the same conclusions can be reached by either doctrine.

7*

The difficulty of giving a physical meaning to the wave functions and characteristic values for the cases where the energy is negative is perhaps due to the attempt to understand them in terms of preconceived notions. They are certainly of importance in the present state of the quantum theory and, to take a particular example, they are essential in the quantum theory of the scattering of light by electrons.

Dirac has made a suggestion in the attempt to give a physical significance to the negative energy states of the electron. He assumes that the states actually exist and that everywhere there are to be found an infinitely large number of electrons in this state. It may be said that what is usually described as empty space is packed with electrons in the negative energy state. From time to time an electron will leave this state in a transition to a positive energy state, in which case an ordinary electron appears. The transition results in an unoccupied energy state or a hole left in the negative states. This hole is observable and its character can be appreciated by reflecting that to obliterate the hole a negative charge and a negative amount of energy are required. The hole therefore appears as something with a positive charge with a positive amount of energy, that is to say, it is the positive counterpart of an electron or a positron. The transition requires a certain amount of energy, for example, energy of radiation, which is converted into a positron and an electron. This type of transition is described as pair production and in the process a quantum of energy $h\nu$ provides $2m_0c^2$ to account for the rest energy of the particles, the excess $(h\nu - 2m_0c^2)$ appearing as their kinetic energy. Such processes are known in physics and appear to occur when gamma rays interact with a strong nuclear field.

The Derivation of the Second Order Equation.—

It is to be expected that some operation on the first order equation will result in a second order equation. It would seem worth while to look for an operation which would derive equation (2.13) from (6.13). The second order equation is to be relativistically invariant and with the approximation of classical mechanics must lead to Schrödinger's equation (2.12). Equation (2.12) is related to the form

$$\text{div}(\text{grad } \psi) = 0$$

if both the operations *grad* and *div* are applied in a four dimensional continuum. These two operations consist in applications of the operator $\left(i_n \dfrac{\partial}{\partial x_n}\right)$ where i_n is a typical vector of a set of four orthogonal unit vectors.

Bearing in mind the similarity between these unit vectors and the matrices of Dirac's equation it is at once suggested that the expression

$$\frac{h}{2\pi i}\cdot\frac{\partial}{\partial t} + \frac{hc}{2\pi i}\left(\alpha_x\frac{\partial}{\partial x} + \alpha_y\frac{\partial}{\partial y} + \alpha_z\frac{\partial}{\partial z}\right) + \beta m_0 c^2$$

should operate upon equation (6.13) remembering that multiplication between the matrices must occur according to rule (6.5) as well as differentiation upon ψ and its differential coefficients. But if this is done it will be found that while the terms containing the first order differential coefficients $\dfrac{\partial \psi}{\partial x}$, $\dfrac{\partial \psi}{\partial y}$, $\dfrac{\partial \psi}{\partial z}$ vanish as a result of the relations (6.7) the term containing $\dfrac{\partial \psi}{\partial t}$ remains. It is, however, the object of the investigation to avoid the introduction of time and space co-ordinates differently. It becomes clear that if the operator

$$\frac{h}{2\pi i}\cdot\frac{\partial}{\partial t} - \frac{hc}{2\pi i}\left(\alpha_x\frac{\partial}{\partial x} + \alpha_y\frac{\partial}{\partial y} + \alpha_z\frac{\partial}{\partial z}\right) - \beta m_0 c^2$$

acts upon (6.13) the result is

$$\left(\frac{h}{2\pi i}\right)^2 \frac{1}{c^2}\frac{\partial^2 \psi}{\partial t^2} - \left(\frac{h}{2\pi i}\right)^2 \nabla^2 \psi - m_0{}^2 c^2 \psi = 0.$$

In the case of a free particle $\dfrac{h}{2\pi i}\dfrac{\partial \psi}{\partial t} = -W\psi$, thus the equation becomes

$$\nabla^2 \psi = -\frac{4\pi^2}{h^2}\left(\frac{W^2}{c^2} - m_0{}^2 c^2\right)\psi = -\frac{4\pi^2}{h^2}p^2\psi,$$

identical with (2.12).

Making use of the notation $P_x = \dfrac{h}{2\pi i}\dfrac{\partial}{\partial x}$, etc., the first order equation can be written in the form :

$$\left\{\frac{H}{c} - (\alpha_x P_x + \alpha_y P_y + \alpha_z P_z + \beta m_0 c)\right\}\psi = 0 \quad (6.18)$$

and the operator upon this equation in the form :

$$\frac{H}{c} + \alpha_x P_x + \alpha_y P_y + \alpha_z P_z + \beta m_0 c.$$

The result of the operation is then

$$\left\{\frac{H^2}{c^2} - (P_x{}^2 + P_y{}^2 + P_z{}^2 + m_0{}^2 c^2)\right\}\psi = 0.$$

In this simple case with ψ in the form of a plane wave,

$$\frac{W^2}{c^2} = p^2 + m_0{}^2 c^2.$$

The First Order Equation for an Electron in an Electromagnetic Field.—In deriving this equation it is necessary to bear in mind the association of the operators P and the co-ordinates. The operators P take the place of the quantity mechanically conjugate to the co-ordinates and referring to the function L of Chapter I it appears that in the simple mechanical cases considered the conjugate to the co-ordinate x is $\dfrac{\partial L}{\partial \dot{x}}$ and that this is equal to the component of momentum $m\dot{x}$, so that in the corresponding equations of wave mechanics the operator P_x replaces the momentum. This is, however, not always the case and it appears from equation (1.14) that in the case of a particle with an electric charge e in an electromagnetic field the conjugate to x is no longer the momentum but the quantity p_x related to it by that equation. Thus the momentum will be replaced by $\left(P_x - \dfrac{e}{c}A_x\right)$ in this case.

The kinetic energy is thus represented by the operator

$$c\left\{\alpha_x\left(P_x - \frac{e}{c}A_x\right) + \alpha_y\left(P_y - \frac{e}{c}A_y\right) + \alpha_z\left(P_z - \frac{e}{c}A_z\right)\right.$$
$$\left. + \beta m_0 c\right\}.$$

In this case there is the additional electrostatic energy $e\phi$, where ϕ is the electrostatic potential. Thus the energy operator $H = -\dfrac{h}{2\pi i}\cdot\dfrac{\partial}{\partial t}$ is now given by

$$H = e\phi + c\left\{\alpha_x\left(P_x - \frac{e}{c}A_x\right) + \alpha_y\left(P_y - \frac{e}{c}A_y\right)\right.$$
$$\left. + \alpha_z\left(P_z - \frac{e}{c}A_z\right) + \beta m_0 c\right\}.$$

Dirac's equation becomes

$$\left(\frac{H}{c} - \frac{e\phi}{c}\right)\psi - \left\{\alpha_x\left(P_x - \frac{e}{c}A_x\right) + \alpha_y\left(P_y - \frac{e}{c}A_y\right)\right.$$
$$\left. + \alpha_z\left(P_z - \frac{e}{c}A_z\right) + \beta m_0 c\right\}\psi = 0$$
$$(6.19)$$

In the special theory of relativity the fourth component of momentum $p_4 = iW/c$, $W = mc^2$ and the fourth component of the electromagnetic potential $\phi_4 = i\phi$. Thus a fourth operator P_4 is suggested, p_4 being replaced by $\left(P_4 - \dfrac{e}{c}\phi_4\right)$ and it would be expected that $P_4 = \dfrac{h}{2\pi i}\cdot\dfrac{\partial}{\partial x_4}$, where $x_4 = ict$ in accordance with the relativistic notation.

Thus $iP_4 = \dfrac{h}{2\pi i} \cdot \dfrac{1}{c} \dfrac{\partial}{\partial t} = -\dfrac{H}{c}$ and equation (6.19) can be written in the form

$$\alpha_n\left(P_n - \frac{e}{c}\phi_n\right)\psi + m_0 c\beta\psi = 0 \qquad . \quad (6.20)$$

where summation is made for $n = 1, 2, 3, 4$ and $(\phi_1, \phi_2, \phi_3) = (A_x, A_y, A_z)$ and $\alpha_4 = i$.

The second order equation in this case is obtained as in the case of equation (6.18) by use of the operator

$$\frac{H}{c} - \frac{e\phi}{c} + \alpha_x\left(P_x - \frac{e}{c}A_x\right) + \alpha_y\left(P_y - \frac{e}{c}A_y\right)$$
$$+ \alpha_z\left(P_z - \frac{e}{c}A_z\right) + \beta m_0 c. \quad (6.21)$$

In order to derive the resulting second order equation it is convenient to write

$$u_n = P_n - \frac{e}{c}\phi_n = \frac{h}{2\pi i}\frac{\partial}{\partial x_n} - \frac{e}{c}\phi_n \qquad . \quad (6.22)$$

so that equation (6.20) takes the form

$$(\alpha_4 u_4 + \alpha_k u_k + m_0 c\beta)\psi = 0, \ (k = 1, 2, 3)$$

and the operator (6.21)

$$- \alpha_4 u_4 + \alpha_l u_l + m_0 c\beta.$$

In this case the summation is for $l = 1, 2, 3$ and to avoid confusion the suffix to be summed is denoted differently in the two brackets. Thus the second order equation is

$$(- \alpha_4 u_4 + \alpha_l u_l + m_0 c\beta)(\alpha_4 u_4 + \alpha_k u_k + m_0 c\beta)\psi = 0 \quad (6.23)$$

If it be remembered that $\beta\alpha_l u_l = \beta\alpha_k u_k$ since l and k are dummy suffixes denoting by their occurrence twice in the same expression that summation occurs and that

$$(\beta\alpha_k + \alpha_k\beta) = 0,$$

the result of the operation is

$$(u_4{}^2\psi + \Sigma u_k{}^2 + m_0{}^2c^2)\psi + i\alpha_l(u_lu_4 - u_4u_l)\psi + \alpha_l\alpha_ku_lu_k\psi = 0, \qquad . \qquad . \quad (6.24)$$

where in the summation in the last term $l \neq k$, the case of equality being represented in the term $\Sigma u_k{}^2\psi$. If the case $l = 2$, $k = 3$ be considered for the purpose of illustration, it will be seen that the last term contains $\alpha_2\alpha_3u_2u_3\psi$, but the last term also includes the case $l = 3$, $k = 2$ i.e. $\alpha_3\alpha_2u_3u_2\psi$. From (6.7) $\alpha_2\alpha_3 = -\alpha_3\alpha_2$ so that these terms together give $\alpha_2\alpha_3(u_2u_3 - u_3u_2)\psi$.

On performing the operation, making use of (6.22) the two terms give $-\alpha_2\alpha_3\dfrac{h}{2\pi i}\dfrac{e}{c}\left(\dfrac{\partial\phi_3}{\partial x_2} - \dfrac{\partial\phi_2}{\partial x_3}\right)$.

From the electromagnetic theory the x-component of the magnetic intensity, $F_x = F_{23} = \left(\dfrac{\partial\phi_3}{\partial x_2} - \dfrac{\partial\phi_2}{\partial x_3}\right)$.

These components are usually denoted by H_x or H_{23} but F is used instead of H in order to avoid confusion with the Hamiltonian.

Thus the two terms give $i\alpha_2\alpha_3\dfrac{he}{2\pi c}F_{23}\psi$.

In the same way the remaining parts of the last term of equation (6.24) are $i\alpha_3\alpha_1\dfrac{he}{2\pi c}F_{31}\psi$ and $i\alpha_1\alpha_2\dfrac{he}{2\pi c}F_{12}\psi$.

Remembering that $E_x = -\dfrac{1}{c}\dfrac{\partial\phi_1}{\partial t} - \dfrac{\partial\phi}{\partial x}$ with corresponding expressions for E_y and E_z, a similar procedure shows that $i\alpha_l(u_lu_4 - u_4u_l)\psi = i\alpha_l\dfrac{he}{2\pi c}E_l,$

where E_1, E_2, $E_3 = E_x$, E_y, $E_z = iF_{14}$, iF_{24}, iF_{34}. Thus equations (6.24) becomes

$$\left(u_4{}^2 + \Sigma u_k{}^2 + m_0{}^2c^2 + \dfrac{he}{2\pi c}\sigma . F + \dfrac{he}{2\pi c}i\alpha . E\right)\psi = 0 \quad (6.25)$$

The expression $\sigma . F$ denotes $(\sigma_x F_x + \sigma_y F_y + \sigma_z F_z)$ where σ_x, σ_y, σ_z denote $i\alpha_2\alpha_3$, $i\alpha_3\alpha_1$, $i\alpha_1\alpha_2$ respectively. In the same way $\alpha . E$ denotes $(\alpha_x E_x + \alpha_y E_y + \alpha_z E_z)$.

The significance of the terms containing the field intensities F and E can be understood by comparison with Schrödinger's non-relativistic equation (2.16). In the case represented by this equation there is no electromagnetic field so that the operators u_k are replaced by P_k. Thus equation (2.16) can be expressed in the form

$$(2im_0cP_4 + \Sigma P_k{}^2 + 2m_0V)\psi = 0 \quad . \quad (6.26)$$

The occurrence of P_4 in the first degree in this expression and of u_4 in the second in equation (6.25) is accounted for by the fact that (6.26) is in the non-relativistic form but it appears that the additional terms of (6.25) correspond to the potential energy term $2m_0V$ so that the equation of the electron in the electromagnetic field indicates the existence of a real energy term of magnitude $\dfrac{he}{4\pi m_0c} (\sigma . F)$.

It should be mentioned that this comparison is somewhat superficial and that a closer examination indicates that the rest mass in this equation should be replaced by the ordinary mass m. In fact, a more careful examination shows that the term $1/m_0$ should be replaced by β/m_0 which is the quantum mechanical equivalent of $1/m$. The present discussion is, however, sufficient to show that the relativistic treatment of the equation of a charged particle introduces a term representing an interaction with the magnetic field and the form of the term suggests an energy term arising from a magnet of moment $\dfrac{he}{4\pi m_0c} \sigma$. If the values of σ_x, σ_y, σ_z are determined from the products of the α matrices from which they are derived, it will be found that $\sigma_x{}^2 = \sigma_y{}^2 = \sigma_z{}^2 = 1$. Thus on squaring $\dfrac{he}{4\pi m_0c} \sigma_x$, etc., it follows that the value of the magnetic moment is $\pm \dfrac{he}{4\pi m_0c}$. If this is applied in the case of the electron the value of the magnetic moment is equal to that resulting from the concept of electron spin introduced by Goudsmit and Uhlenbeck to account for the doublets occurring in the alkali spectra.

It thus appears that Dirac's derivation of the first order equation based on the principle of relativity accounts without further hypothesis for an intrinsic magnetic moment. When the charge and mass of the electron are introduced into the equation the energy value resulting from its solution is that of an electron in an electromagnetic field. The equation represents the electron in its inter-action with the field.

The case of great interest is that of the electron in the hydrogen atom where the electromagnetic field is represented by a central attraction according to the inverse square law.

The solution of this case has been obtained by C. G. Darwin,[1] and the characteristic values of the energy, E, have been derived. These may be written in the approximate form :

$$E = - \frac{2\pi^2 m_0 e^4}{h^2 n^2} \left\{ 1 + \frac{\alpha^2}{n^2} \left(\frac{n}{j + \frac{1}{2}} - \frac{3}{4} \right) \right\},$$

where n is the integer which enters into the formula in the same way as into formula (4.25) derived from Schrödinger's equation, and is the total quantum number. It will be noticed that this energy value is similar in form to that derived by Sommerfeld in his theory of the fine structure of the hydrogen spectrum (6.1). It differs in one particular only, but the difference is important. The azimuthal quantum number k is replaced by $(j + \frac{1}{2})$, j denoting the so-called inner quantum number. j has the values $(l \pm \frac{1}{2})$. Suppose $l = 2$, a value for j in this case is $j = (l - \frac{1}{2}) = 3/2$, but if $l = 1$, j can have the value $(l + \frac{1}{2}) = 3/2$. Thus although the number l has different values in this case for any given value of n, the values of E are the same.

[1] *Proc. Roy. Soc.*, 1928, **118**, p. 654.

In transitions j can change by ± 1 or 0 and in the case of the hydrogen and helium line spectra this leads to the correct number of lines in the fine structure as well as the correct line displacement. Some of these transitions coincide with those which can be derived by means of Sommerfeld's theory. As an example, the case of a transition from $n = 3, j = 3/2$ to $n = 2, j = \frac{1}{2}$ has the same energy change as that from $n = 3, l = 2$ to $n = 2, l = 1$ in applying Sommerfeld's formula. Nevertheless the later theory shows that Sommerfeld's formula is fundamentally, although not quantitatively, incorrect.

REFERENCES

G. BIRTWISTLE. The New Quantum Mechanics. (Camb. Univ. Press, 1928.)

N. BOHR. Das Quantenpostulat und die neuere Entwicklung der Atomistik. (*Naturwissenschaften*, Art. 453.)

N. BOHR. The Quantum Postulate, and the Recent Development of Atomic Theory. (*Nature*, Vol. 121, Ap. 1928, p. 589.)

L. DE BROGLIE. Sur le parallelisme entre la dynamique du point materiel et l'optique géométrique. (*J. de Physique*, 6ᵉ Série, t. vii, 1926, p. 1.)

L. DE BROGLIE. Introduction to Wave Mechanics. (Methuen.)

F. BROUWER, Wellenmechanische Eigenwertprobleme. (*Ann. d. Physik*, 84, p. 915.)

P. A. M. DIRAC. Roy. Soc. Proc., A, 117, p. 610. Quantum Mechanics. (Clarendon Press.)

L. FLAMM. Die Grundlage der Wellenmechanik. *Phys. Zeitscher.*, 27 Jahrg., p. 600.)

J. FRENKEL. Einführung in die Wellenmechanik. (Berlin, Julius Springer.)

W. HEISENBERG. Uber den anschaulichen Inhalt u.s.w. (*Z. f. Physik*, 43, 1927, p. 172.)

O. W. RICHARDSON. On the Present State of Atomic Physics. (*Proc. Phys. Soc.*, 39, p. 171.)

E. SCHRÖDINGER. Quantisierung als Eigenwertproblem. (*Ann. d. Physik*, 79, 1926, p. 489.) Uber das Verhältnis des Heisenberg - Born - Jordansche Quantenmechanik zu der meinen. (*Ann. d. Physik*, 79, 1926, p. 734.) Der stetige Ubergang von der Mikro- zur Makromechanik. (*Naturwissenchaften*, 14 Jahrg., p. 664.)

G. P. THOMSON. Experiments on the Diffraction of Cathode Rays. (*Roy. Soc. Proc.*, A, 117, p. 600.)

B. L. WORSNOP. Note on the Transmission of Cathode Rays through Thin Films. (*Proc. Phys. Soc.*, June, 1928.)

BORN. Atomic Physics. 4th Edn. 1946. (Blackie & Son Ltd.)

TEMPLE. General Principles of Quantum Theory. (Methuen's Monographs, 1951.)

L. DE BROGLIE. L'Electron Magnetique. (Gauthier Villars, 1933.)

DIRAC. Quantum Mechanics. 3rd Edn. (Clarendon Press.)

HEITLER. Wave Mechanics. (Clarendon Press, 1945.)

FRENKEL. Wave Mechanics, Elementary Theory. (Dover Publications, 1950.)

INDEX

PRINTED IN GREAT BRITAIN AT
THE UNIVERSITY PRESS
ABERDEEN